BOOKS BY JOHN McNULTY

THIRD AVENUE, NEW YORK

A MAN GETS AROUND

A Man Gets Around

A Man Gets Around

JOHN McNULTY

Little, Brown and Company · Boston · 1951

To my son Johnny,
at this time eight weeks old.
He has a good left jab,
but his straight right
leaves something to be desired.

These stories have appeared in, and are published through the courtesy of, *The New Yorker*.

Foreword

Wʜᴇɴ the Little, Brown people said they were willing to come out with another collection of pieces I had written for *The New Yorker,* the next thing I had to do before I could get some betting-money out of the idea was to think of a title. As anybody with half an eye can see, we wound up with *A Man Gets Around.*

Possibly that may need some explanation because titles usually do. The explanation is that the Little, Brown people — and if you say that out loud, it sounds as if they were a Filipino outfit, instead of being on Beacon Street, Boston — are a logical bunch, and they like to have the name on the cover of a book have something to do with what is inside the book.

Inside this book is a piece about going to Kentucky

and a piece about going to Ireland, and another about going to Wakefield, Rhode Island, and one about going to Bellevue Hospital. In addition, there are stories — or, as they call them on *The New Yorker,* "casuals" — about people here and there and about small happenings in New York, N. Y.

To dope out a title, I started with saying to myself, "What *is* all this stuff?" Some pretty vague answers came, until they all boiled down into a kind of singsong which, of itself, made too long a title but did express some notion of what the book's about: "A Man Gets Around, Sees This and That, Hears One Person Say One Thing and Another Person Another, and He Puts It Down the Best He Can, and First Thing He Knows It's Some Kind of Book." That is altogether too many words for a title, so we collapsed it down to "A Man Gets Around."

JOHN McNULTY

Contents

Foreword   ix

      PART I   *A Man Gets Around*

1 Back Where I Had Never Been   3

2 Where the Grass, They Say, Is Blue   38

3 Bellevue Days   58

4 The Jackpot   86

      PART II   *People*

1 Overlooked Lady   123

2 Slightly Crocked   129

3 Mrs. Carmody's Store   136

4 Müller with an Umlaut   148

5 Yellow-Ball-in-the-Side   155

Contents

PART III   *Happenings in New York*

1   Can't Slip Any Drugs to Sisters on Fifth
Avenue   167

2   Third Avenue Medicine   171

3   The Television Helps, but Not Very Much   175

PART I

A Man Gets Around

I

~~~~~~

Back Where I Had Never Been

~~~~~~

My wife and I recently returned from a sentimental excursion to Ireland. All my life, friends have called me "Irishman," because of my name, McNulty, and since before this summer I had never been in Ireland and knew little or nothing about the Irish, except those of Third Avenue and Boston, I felt like a fake. Now I have spent a couple of months in Ireland, and while I still am no Irish authority, a few small things did happen to me there that recurringly please my mind, and I feel better for having gone there.

How we came to go was that we had a windfall of about four thousand dollars. The money was so unexpected that we had a joint impulse to waste it. Perhaps not to waste it, exactly, but to spend it on unnecessary things rather than put it aside in fearful anticipation of a disaster, four-thousand-dollar size. "We'll dribble it away," I said venturously, "with an automobile here and a new suit there, and a television set we don't want, and, first thing we know, it'll all be gone and nothing to show for it." "We could go to Ireland," my wife said, and I was astonished. "I have an idea you've always wanted to go to Ireland," she went on, "but when I think of it, I don't ever remember your saying so in so many words." This was a joyful surprise to me, because my wife is only a small part Irish, the other parts being New England Yankee and English and French.

I myself am what the Irish call a Narrowback. The term is neither praiseful nor disdainful. It is merely a sorrowful truth about us American men who were born here of parents who came from Ireland. In nine hundred and ninety-nine cases out of a thousand, our fathers came to this country with small education but broad backs and strong muscles, prepared to do such work in the United States as called for this equipment. Succeeding here to a greater or lesser degree, they gave us, their American-born sons, as much schooling as they could, and with some education we turned to less laborious means of earning a living. So, figuratively or literally, through an accelerated process of evolution favored by the Irish, our backs grew narrower. It is my belief that every Narrowback is pleasurably haunted by the notion that someday he will go and see about Ireland for himself. When my wife said what she did, I replied, "That's the thing to do — go to Ireland. And let's have no more concern over what happens to our little box of money." "That's right," she said. "The hell with it." A strange thing for a wife to say, but a most pleasant thing to hear.

The trip decided upon, my first impulse was to noise the news modestly around our neighborhood, at Seventy-second Street and Second Avenue. Everybody knows Ireland is only twelve or thirteen hours away by plane, but a trip to Ireland seemed to me a sizable project. Besides, I didn't want to go by plane. I wanted it to be farther away than thirteen hours, and we'd go by ship and have a lot of talking about it beforehand. Our neighborhood, which comprises a certain few blocks where we know each other, by sight anyway, is small and nicely gossipy. I started the news around by going to Maxie Slavin, the tireless little hundred-and-fourteen-pound man who runs the newsstand at the corner of Second.

"I want you to stop sending the papers to the house, Maxie," I said.

"What's the matter?" he asked. "Any trouble?"

"Oh, no, no," I said. "We're going away for a couple months. We're going to Ireland."

Maxie smiled a big grin. He comes from Minsk. I noticed an odd thing in the next few weeks: when you tell people you're going to Ireland, they smile almost as if they were going themselves. I imagine that if you say you're going to Paris, people say something like "Oh boy, oh boy!" with the implication that you're going to polish off all the women and drink up all the wine. When you say England, maybe they say "Yeah?" When it's Ireland, they smile. I don't know why this is.

"Gee whizz! Ireland!" said Maxie. "Galway Bay! Blarney Castle! Going to Ireland, huh? You're a lucky guy! It's a great spot, they say. When you going?"

"I don't know yet. In a few weeks, maybe. Just beginning the arrangements," I said.

"Well, why am I going to stop the papers so soon?" he asked. "You could tell me just before you go away'll be time enough."

"That's right," I said. "I'll let you know."

It was probably a bad way to start the news around the neighborhood, but it was the only one I could think of.

The news got around. I went to the shop of Mark Tribus, the Jewish barber who always cuts my hair. "I hear you're going to Ireland," Mark said. "You going to Dublin?"

"Sure we'll be in Dublin," I said.

"Right away I'll write a letter to my nephew," he said.

"In Dublin?" I asked dubiously.

"A man's going to Ireland, will I write a letter to a nephew in Chicago?" Mark said. "Certainly in Dublin! He got a big furniture business. A big man in Dublin, my nephew. Right away I'll write him."

"Do that, Mark," I said.

Part of the pleasant preparations was having a talk with a friend who was born and brought up in Ireland

and in whose counsel I have great confidence. He is Timothy Athena Costello, who runs what he calls a "store," or saloon, at Forty-fourth Street and Third Avenue. (The "Athena," his confirmation name, was given him in honor of a nun in Ferbane, County Offaly, where he was reared.) We spread a large map of Ireland on the bar and together scrutinized it, I with the eyes of a greenhorn, he with knowledge harking back to the period years ago when he was the driver of cars rented to visitors in Dublin.

"It'll be raining most of the time," Tim said. "Do you have only a skimpy raincoat, or have you something with a little weight and warmth to it?"

"Skimpy," I said.

"Then first thing is get a raincoat," he said. "It'll rain every day, and it'll be cold in the mornings and evenings, especially cold for Americans. A hefty raincoat, the first thing."

He took a pencil and made rings around four or five places on the coast. Then, with an appalling gesture of dismissal, he swept his hand down through the whole middle of Ireland. "This," he said, "you can skip. You'd find it very tiresome and dull. The coast is grand." It was as if on a map of the States he had eradicated in one motion all America between the Rockies and the Appalachians.

"Tell me this," Tim said, dropping his pencil near Cork. "How do you feel about Blarney Castle?"

"I am determined to avoid Blarney Castle at all costs," I replied. "I'm sick of hearing about it and I think it's the bunk. That isn't the Ireland I want to see."

"Ha-ha!" he said. "Then you'll have a glorious time in Ireland. The place is not all Mother Machree and that sort of thing."

"I don't want it to be Mother Machree," I said. "I don't go at all for Mother Machree. Don't misunderstand me, now. She's probably all right in her place, but on all those Saint Patrick's Days, all those years of meeting synthetic Gaels around saloons, I got terribly sick of Mother Machree. I hope there'll be very little of Mother Machree on this trip."

"I don't misunderstand you," said Tim. "A minimum of Mother Machree is what you mean, a minimum of Mother Machree. Will you do as I tell you and go get a warm raincoat?"

"I will," I said.

So I went over to Brooks Brothers and bought a handsome raincoat for seventy-five dollars. Ordinarily, I would never dream of buying that class of raincoat, but that's the way I felt, and I even bought a detachable woollen lining, which cost fifteen dollars. The rain that makes Ireland so green also made this coat a good investment.

A night or so before we were to sail, my wife put our guidebook down on the arm of her chair and said, "I was thinking about the drinking. I don't want to be a dry blanket, but don't you think you might really enjoy it more over there if you did no drinking? I have the impression they do quite a lot of it over there."

"I've always had the same idea," I said. "Probably

you're right. No doubt you're right. And I've been thinking about their complicated politics, too. It certainly
would be unwise for a stranger like me to go talking Irish
politics in Dublin, or wherever we might be."

So I made two resolutions for the trip, as follows:

1. No drinking in Ireland.
2. No talking Irish politics in Ireland.

As it turned out, it was quite some time before I began
talking Irish politics in Ireland.

On board our ship, the *Britannic*, we became friends
with a six-foot-three American, David Mellor, who comes
from Natick, Massachusetts, and was on the Dartmouth
crew in his college days, which are only a few years back.
Mellor told us that he did not have one drop of Irish
blood in him but that since boyhood he had read everything Irish he could get his hands on — poetry, history,
plays, stories — and that this had aroused in him an irre-
sistible desire to visit Ireland, which he was about to do.
He planned to bicycle all over the place for two or three
months. Mellor could recite Yeats by the half hour, and
his fervor for Ireland was amazing. It is hard to believe
that any returning Irishman could be as eager to reach
Ireland as Mellor was.

When the tender that took us from the *Britannic* at
last touched the dock at Cobh, Mellor was way up front,
anxious to be among the first passengers to step on Irish
soil. In Ireland, flowers seem determined to grow. They
pop up out of crevices in the flagstone walks, they peek

out of soil-filled cracks in ancient walls, and they even blossom, unasked, out of the roofs of cottages. So it was that bright, yellowy blooms were growing in a tiny space at the edge of the dock, in the cracks of the stone walks. Mellor's foot touched the dock, and his eyes widened as he looked down. "Jeepers cripes!" he said. "An Irish dandylion!" And he leaned over and examined it with delight, as if it were something new and strange, something he had been waiting a long time to see, and here it was at last. "An Irish dandylion!" he said a few times more.

In Counihan's snug, near the Imperial Hotel, in Cork, the Corkonian next to me at the bar was reading the *Irish Times*. "Did you see this?" he asked, looking at me over his spectacles. He pointed to a story about the Minister for Agriculture, who on the evening before had said in an address that the farmers were doing fine with the cattle and fine with the pigs but that they would have to do better with eggs. More and more eggs must be produced to be sold to England and other countries, to bolster the finances of this beginning republic of Ireland.

"I read it this morning," I said.

"That's the latest scheme they have around here now," he said, and a glint came into his eyes.

"What's that?" I dutifully asked.

"Drown the English in a wave of eggs!" he roared. "It's a horrible death! Drowning in a wave of eggs! I doubt the English deserve such an end as that!"

* * *

Most mornings, at the Gresham Hotel in Dublin, we were awakened early by sea gulls and "Buttons and Bows." Every morning, I thought about how we have sea gulls back home in Manhattan, too. There were hundreds of them over around First Avenue and Forty-fourth and Forty-fifth Streets when the slaughterhouses were on the spot where they're building the United Nations Headquarters. But our sea gulls seem to keep off the main streets. In Dublin, they wheel ceaselessly over O'Connell Street, dipping down from time to time onto the River Liffey, and every morning they are screaming as they search for breakfast. Invariably we would hear, mingled with their screeches, the sound of an early worker hustling along the street whistling "Buttons and Bows." It was not an unpleasant awakening at all, and each morning it fell into a pattern, part of which went like this in my train of drowsy thought: There go the sea gulls, over the Liffey. Oh, yes, the Liffey: O'er the Liffey's swell. . . . Now, how did that song go?

> And the Angelus bell
> O'er the Liffey's swell,
> Rang out in the morning dew. . . .

That is a song I had often heard in the bars-and-grills of Third Avenue. The Angelus bell o'er the Liffey's swell was the signal for the Easter uprising of long ago, according to this song, the singing of which was once forbidden in Ireland, and that made it a very popular song to sing. And now, I would think, I am in Dublin, and not far from the Liffey. In a couple of minutes I can walk down to the General Post Office and see, on the great pillars before it, the marks of the bullets that scarred those walls during "The Trouble."

Nobody in Dublin took me around to see such things as the bullet marks. Nobody, of all the Irishmen I met, conveyed any impression of hatred of the English, with whom those battles on the streets of Dublin were fought. It was back on Third Avenue that I had heard such things — had heard long-distance Irish patriotism expressing itself in great blasts (verbal) against the English. On Third Avenue, many is the time I had heard the phrase "the goddam English." Never once did I hear it in Ireland. For one thing, it seems to me that I heard mighty little swearing in Ireland anyway, and when, in a pub or some such place, I dropped a few profane words into my speech, from force of habit, I had a sense of being offensive, and I soon learned to curb myself. And, for another thing, the feeling distinctly came to me in Ireland that this struggle against the English has been going on too long — eight hundred years or so — to be encompassed in any superficial loud talk belittling so steadfast an enemy.

Enemy? Yes, I suppose so. Yet I heard in Ireland frequent expressions of sympathy for the English in their economic plight, their dire need of a varied diet. Ireland is full of English families seeking food. In talks with visiting Englishmen, I learned that the austere diet of England makes parents worry about the health of their children, even when they can overlook the wearying effect a meager allotment of meat has upon themselves.

Many fairly well-to-do English families arrange to spend a week or so in Ireland every once in a while, so that they can "feed up" in a country where meat and butter are abundant. That is good for the economy of this new republic of Ireland, because when an Englishman goes to Ireland, he may take an unlimited number of pounds to spend, even though if he is going elsewhere in Europe, his limit is fifty pounds.

One morning, I sat at a table next to an English family of four — father, mother, young son, and young daughter — and I gathered from their easily overheard conversation that they had arrived the night before and this was their first meal in Ireland. Here is what each of them ate: a large dish of oatmeal and cream and sugar, a mackerel, three or four slices of cold roast beef, bacon and eggs, plenty of buttered bread, with marmalade, and, of course, pots and pots of tea. They ate ravenously.

Their waiter was also mine. In between his servings, he stood by in his tail coat (in Ireland waiters often wear tails even at breakfast) and with a gentle, thoughtful look on his face watched the English eat. When the bacon and eggs were finished, he went to the table, and I heard him say, "Could I get you some more eggs, sir? The children seem to be hungry still. Let me run out and get you some more eggs." And he did. Afterward, he came over to my table and said to me in a low voice, "It's pitiful to see them so hungry, now, isn't it, sir? The poor children seem starved with the hunger. D'ye know, sir, I'm really sorry for them!" The waiter was old enough to have been in The Trouble. I had a feeling that he had been in it, fighting the English on the streets of Dublin, or maybe of Cork. Now he was sorry for them. It wasn't at all like Third Avenue, there on O'Connell Street.

Trinity College is right in the middle of Dublin, on College Green. To the same extent that I did not want to see Blarney Castle, I did want to see Trinity College. So here I was, standing across the street from it. Beyond the open gates were two statues, which I knew to be of Oliver Goldsmith and Edmund Burke, both graduates. In the middle of the street, like a tall rock, was a cop around whom an endless flood of bicycles swirled. There were lots of times in Ireland when I was conscious of not wanting to barge into places. I never wanted to barge into a countryman's white cottage, however appealing it was as we passed in our rented car. I didn't want to barge into Trinity, either. I went out into the street and spoke to the cop. He took his arms out from where they were folded majestically under his cape and saluted as I approached. "Would it be all right for me to go into Trinity?" I asked. "I'm not a student. I'm an American visitor."

"Ho, ho!" the cop said. "That wouldn't be my business at all. That's private property, sir, and, of course, I have nothing to do with it at all!" He smiled, yet he conveyed the idea that he was imparting a piece of valuable knowledge. He waved a bevy of bicycles by.

"Oh," I said.

"You understand, sir," the cop said, in more patient explanation, "I would not have a thing to do with a place that is private property. You could go in there as far as I'm concerned, and they could hang you if they felt like it, and do you understand, sir, it wouldn't be my place to lift a hand about it? Private property."

"I guess I'll go in," I said, and started toward the gates.

"Very well, sir," the cop said, and quickly blocked off a surge of bicycles for me. An instant later he shouted after me, "I don't think they'll hang you!"

At the gate there was a porter in a uniform that included a Prince Albert coat, and he told me that it was perfectly proper for visitors to go in and wander about. "Be sure and see the Book of Kells," he said. It was sunny, but the gray walls of all the old buildings around the quadrangle looked chilly, the way a gray sea can look chilly even in summer, with the sun beating down on it. Trinity is a busy and peaceful place, both at the same time. Students wear black gowns to classes, and sometimes go by on bicycles with their gowns flying behind them, like the robes of Bedouins on horses.

The Book of Kells has been described as the most beautiful book in the world, and all my life I've been hearing about it. The attendant in the library, which is upstairs in an aura of lovely mustiness, took me over to the Book, along with an elderly English couple, both of them tall and tweeded. The Book was under glass, opened to a breath-taking page. The attendant held a magnifying glass over it, so that we three could see the marvels of it, the fineness, the unbelievable beauty of the gold and rich blue and deep green of the coloring, so enhanced by the kindliness of a dozen centuries. The attendant explained that the Book was illuminated by the monks of the town of Kells in the eighth century or thereabouts. It is the Gospels.

"Quite good, quite good!" the Englishman said when the attendant paused. The Englishman did not mean the slightest harm. But is that a thing to say of such a wondrous work — "Quite good, quite good"? No harm in him, I repeat, but he managed to imply that if the Book had been done in England, it would have been done slightly better. The attendant, surely an Irishman, looked at me wordlessly, and I at him. It was one of the few times in Ireland when I felt like a thorough Irishman. The attendant and I smiled at the Englishman. "It *is* quite good," the attendant said.

I walked away and for a few minutes stood by myself in the library. This room has a feeling of bold serenity, you might say. Only one other place I've ever been felt like it — that room in Philadelphia where the Declaration of Independence was signed. I rejoined our group, and the attendant showed us a Bible printed in Ireland centuries ago. A small thing was the most interesting thing about that Bible. Others say "There is no balm in Gilead," but this early Irish Bible says "There is no treacle in Gilead."

I gave the attendant half a crown before I left. He took it and said, "Is there anything you fancy at the Phoenix Park races this afternoon, sir?"

Does a two-dollar horse player wear a neon sign on his forehead that says HORSE PLAYER?

"I haven't even looked at the entries yet," I said, and

I went out through the gates and, crossing the street, passed the cop.

"Did you see the Book of Kells?" he asked.

In a public square in Galway City there is a statue, modestly done, of a compact little man. He is sitting on a wall, with a bucolic hat on, an angular, countrified suit, and common, thick-soled shoes, and he is in a contemplative pose, his eyes looking down, and a quiet air about him. This is the statue of a storyteller. That's what he did; he went around the country with an ass and a cart, telling stories. His name was Padraic O'Conaire. His was a simple yet noble calling, I think, and they must have thought so in Galway, too, for there's the statue, and while I am not much of a traveler, and so do not know for sure, I doubt if anywhere else in the world there is a statue in tribute to a man who merely told stories to those who would listen.

I had heard that back in the mountains, away from the cities, in small, Gaelic-speaking communities, there are still storytellers, men locally famed for their ability to sit by the fire and entertain their neighbors with narratives. So every now and then I would make an effort to find one. In Waterville, which is a seaside resort on the southwest coast, in County Kerry, I spoke to the barmaid in the Butler Arms Hotel about this matter. (That's a good way to begin any quest in Ireland, I learned — speak to the barmaid about it.)

"I am sure, sir, that Tadg Murphy would know about things like that," she said. "He's on the Irish

Folklore Commission, and he lives just up the road a way."

The barmaid went back to humming *"Mañana,"* with no more thought for Irish folklore, and after a Guinness I went on out and found Tadg Murphy's house. His first name is pronounced "Tige," as if it were short for "Tiger," and it is the Gaelic version of "Timothy." He is a soft-voiced, scholarly man, whose wife's brother lives in the Bronx. Murphy, who speaks the Gaelic language, has spent years going about in the rural parts of Ireland, seeking to preserve the vanishing lore and making written records of ways of life that are disappearing. He promised to find an Irish storyteller and take my wife and me to hear him.

A day or two later, the three of us met at noon and drove for an hour or so, to the foot of a mountain by the sea. Then we walked up past a farm on the slope, through mist and rain, to a fine, substantial cottage. Two dogs came out to wag us in. Within — and it was warm after the chill rain of the mountain outside — was the scene so well known to millions who have never been in Ireland — the white-washed walls, the turf fire burning, the dogs and the children at their ease upon the floor, the furniture simple and scrubbed, many holy pictures, pictures cheaply made but sincerely revered, on the walls. An old man was seated by the fire, his back as straight as the haft of a T square, his cane in his hand, and his eyes as young as if he were twenty-five; they were not the blue Irish eyes, but gray-green. He was, we were told, eighty-one years old, and his name was O'Connor, the

English form, coincidentally, of "O'Conaire," of the Galway statue.

Murphy explained to him that the Americans wanted to hear him tell a story, and he demurred, only slightly, on the ground that if we did not understand Irish, what would be the sense of his telling a story in that language to us, and it the only language he ever told stories in? Murphy offered to translate from the Irish to us, and the old man began.

"I will tell you a story of a young man who let a great anger be born inside him against the sea and what happened by reason of that," he said, according to Murphy. "He was strong and bold, and there was a great deal of goodness in him, even though he had the mischief that has to go with sailing on the sea, which he did; and he was a fisherman."

This was the first time I had ever heard the Irish language spoken at any length. It did not seem to me a melodious language; it seemed guttural. Every once in a while — and there is no foundation for the resemblance in philology, of course — it sounded like Yiddish.

"Now, I will not tell you of their courtship," the old man said, "because that was a matter between the two of them and not for us at all, but in time the young fisherman married the most wholesome, handsome young woman of his village, which is not far from where we are all sitting, by this very fire, although the village is down by the edge of the sea itself. God sent them a lovely child, and the two of them were happy with the little one, and the father, home from his fishing, would carry the baby in his arms, with his wife walking behind them, on the two streets of the village, so everyone could see — back and forth, back and forth, on the two streets, of a Sunday or even in the twilight on other days."

The children were quiet as he told his story, and so were the rest of us. His daughter-in-law was attentive, and yet all the while she was baking bread. A large iron kettle sat on the burning turf. Upon its heavy lid, four or five oblong pieces of glowing turf had been placed, and so an oven had been made of the kettle. From time to time, but without interrupting the story, the daughter-in-law would go to the fire and deftly lift the lid — burning turf and all — with tongs, and reach in and move the large loaf baking inside, then replace the lid. She was smoking a Sweet Afton cigarette.

"The young fisherman went to sea in his boat, and his comrades with him," the old man said. "And his beautiful wife and his dear child were down by the water's edge to watch the boat go farther and farther away, and at last they could see it no more. Now, that was the time an evil sickness put its cold hand on that village. One after another of the people died, young and old alike. It was only four days the young fisherman was away on the sea. All the same, in that short time what happened was so bad there was nobody in that village had the courage to meet him, when at last his boat came in, and tell him. His darling wife and the child were dead. He went home alone, nobody to meet him, and he found out in that minute he was always going to be alone — no more wife and child for him. The young fisherman was swallowed by sorrow and madness.

"Now, I will not tell of the wake and how deep-stricken the young man was, because you know that and you can think it more truly than I can tell it in my poor way. What you do not know, and I'll tell you, is that when his dear ones were buried and him alone, this terrible anger against the sea came on. One day not long after, when he had the drink taken, he was seen by his friends on a lonely part of the strand, standing with his feet in the water, and he was shaking his fist at the sea and roaring curses upon it. They heard him say this to the sea — they heard him say, 'I hate you and hate you and hate you, and so I'll beat you always. I'll go back upon you and I'll beat you. You'll try to take my boat, and I'll beat you and bring my boat home to the land again. You'll try to take me and you'll try to drown me, but you'll never have me, because I'll beat you, and I'll walk the land alone until I die in my bed. I hate you and hate you and hate you. You kept me away while my dear ones were dying, and if I had been here, I would have saved them and not let them perish.' That is what the poor, unfortunate man was roaring at the sea, and who could blame him for that?"

As the storyteller went on, his words took on a discernible rhythm and cadence. His dramatic pauses were magnificent, and now and then he would strike his cane vigorously upon the hearth, and the children by the fire would look up and stare. I tingled with the anger imparted by the storyteller as he repeated the young fisherman's mad talk to the sea.

"Away he went, back to his fishing," the old man continued. "But that is not the end of my story. A big storm came in two days and the village was full of fear. And it was rightly so, because all of them were drowned, the young fisherman and all his comrades. In a bay far away, his body was washed up not long after, and it had not been touched by the monstrous fish that commonly devour the drowned people in the sea."

Two Irish words became familiar to me as I listened to the old man talk. One was *agus,* which means "and." Many sentences, coming after pauses, began with *agus.* I had noticed that before, in translations of Irish stories. The other word was *seadh,* pronounced almost like "sha," and it means "yes" or "so." It also began many sentences.

"They brought the young man's body back to his village and they buried him in the cemetery there," the storyteller said. "Now I must tell you how it was with this cemetery. A finger of land stretched out into the water. Now, on the side of this finger of land that was farthest away from the sea was the most peaceful place in all that village. And so it was there that for centuries and centuries the dead of that village had been buried. Never in all the time there was an Ireland had the waters been any other way than most serene there where the cemetery was. Not a handful of land had ever been stolen away by the sea coming in, although the cemetery spread quietly down to within a few feet of the water. So, nine days after the young fisherman was buried, in the grave nearest by the water, the most terrible storm in all memory arose. Three days it went on, and never had anybody seen the like of it. For the first time ever, it happened, the monstrous waves reached over the finger of land. All the people stayed far back from the sea and prayed for the end of the storm. So, the storm ended at last and the people went out. And they stood silent when they saw the great havoc the sea had brought about. It was not at the bigness of the damage that they were frightened and struck silent. It was at this — it was that the mountainy waves of the storm, the clutching hands of the sea, had reached in and torn away one grave. It was the grave of the fisherman who had shaken his fist at the sea, and his coffin was gone and never again was it seen."

Slowly the old man swept his keen eyes around at his listeners to signify the end of his story.

We thanked him and got up to go.

"You'll have some tea?" the daughter-in-law asked timidly after she had lifted the kettle of bread from the fire. We said that it would be too much trouble for her and anyway our dinner was waiting for us back at the hotel.

"You'll not leave my house without having a cup of tea and some bread and butter," said the old man sternly, in English. We had it, and it was fine tea and fine bread and butter.

We bade the daughter-in-law good-by at the door and started to go out into the rain, the two dogs wagging farewell as they had wagged a welcome. Suddenly, the old man, who had remained seated, appeared at the door.

He took me by the arm and addressed me in his slow, halting, but precise English. "Do you see what I have done?" he asked softly. "Without passing a solid thing from my hand to yours, I have put words into your head, and they're the words of a story. Now you will carry the story back in your head to America, and perhaps you will tell the story, too, or perhaps you will write it down. And after a while I will die, but over in America will be a story of mine going around, without ever stopping from going, one to another, and so I won't be dead at all, in one way of thinking it. That's what I have done this day. God bless!"

When anybody asks one of us Narrowbacks why we are going to Ireland, we usually say we want to see the little village our parents came from. That was one thing in my mind when my wife and I were planning our trip. My father came from County Clare, from the region around a town whose name does not sound or look Irish to an American; it is Lisdoonvarna. My mother came from around Ballyhaunis, which is a town in Mayo. (In Gaelic, the prefix "Bally-" means "town of.") Now, to come right down to it, I've never known much more about their birthplaces than these names. Other Narrowbacks I've talked to are in the same fix; we're pretty vague about background. Vague or not, there's quite a pull back to those places. Over the years, in the rare times when my eyes fell on a map of Ireland, two names stuck out from the hundreds — Lisdoonvarna and Ballyhaunis.

But on the *Britannic,* going over, I began to shy

away from Lisdoonvarna. The guidebook described it as "renowned for its Spa," and said: "Attention centers on the recent analysis made by Dr. Monroe, F.I.C., of Bath (England), an acknowledged authority of spas, who found that all the waters of Lisdoonvarna contain the very valuable therapeutic element iodine, in addition to their other constituents."

My people were of the soil, and I never connected them with spas and the resorty air that goes with them. This bit of prose about Lisdoonvarna was far from the white-cottage, burning-peat reveries of years; so, as I say, I began to shy away from Lisdoonvarna. We never did get to Lisdoonvarna. Ballyhaunis was something else again. I really wanted to go there, and one day when we were in Mayo, fairly early in the morning, we headed for the town my mother came from. As we got near Ballyhaunis, it was evident that it was a market day. Many donkey-drawn carts were on the road, going toward the town, and we passed several caravans of tinkers — Irish gypsies — in their covered wagons, their numerous children happily sprawling over these wagons or trudging along the road. In one wagon, we counted fourteen children. "It's no wonder people used to believe that gypsies stole children," my wife observed. "It doesn't seem reasonable that they would have so many of their own."

The square of Ballyhaunis, a small place, was busy and crowded with pigs and people. This was the day, luckily for us, set aside each month for the sale of pigs to the agents of big bacon firms and pork-butchers. Well, the great thing for me about those few hours in Ballyhaunis was that the minute I got away from the automobile, purposely deserting my not-wholly-Irish wife, I felt at home, felt just right, felt as if I belonged there. It smelled right, the faces looked right, and I, the fellow from Seventy-second and Second who seldom, if ever, sees a pig, suddenly had the notion that I knew quite a lot about them as I wandered by the carts and peeked in at the small pigs, and stared down at the sows lying on the cobblestones beside the carts.

I stopped by a young farmer in his late twenties who had a litter of pigs in his cart. He didn't speak to me, but he seemed friendly as he waited for a buyer to come by. "How much would all the pigs bring you, do you think?" I ventured to ask him after standing around a while.

"I'm wanting twenty-eight pounds," he said. "Tell me, sir, do you think I should go to Milwaukee?"

For a while I had almost forgotten I was an American. My clothes and my tongue, evidently, hadn't forgotten what they were. "I don't know," I said. "Do you have a little place of your own here — a little farm? And how are you getting along? I imagine you have relatives in Milwaukee, and that's why you ask."

"I have a cousin there, and he's after asking me to come over," the farmer said. "Do you think it's the wise thing to do, sir?"

"I was wondering if you had a little place of your own here, as I said," I replied.

"I do," said the farmer, "and it's comfortable. In our own way of comfort, I'd want to explain to you."

"Then, since you asked me, I'd say to stay here," I

said. "It isn't all like the movies, back in the States."

"That's the way I've been thinking myself," he said. "The cinema does be painting it up a glorious place, sir. Still and all, they're not picking the money up in the streets, I know."

"They're not," I said.

Up came a buyer, brisk and fat, a pad of paper in one hand, a pencil in the other. Buyer and seller greeted each other like old acquaintances; the buyer looked at the pigs and scribbled some figures on a sheet of his pad and handed it to my friend. But the farmer put his hands behind him. The buyer shoved the piece of paper in the breast pocket of the farmer's homespun jacket and walked away with lively formality. The paper stuck out of the jacket, and I was standing close enough so that I could see the figure "27" on the paper. I was tempted to start talking, but then two other men came up to the farmer and I realized that a ritual was going on, too important to interrupt. These two men, as I found out later, were the "middlemen" traditional in Irish market transactions. They asked the farmer if he would "split the pound," and although I failed to catch an answer, they must have caught one, because up came the buyer again. He flicked the paper from the farmer's pocket and wrote on it. I peeked, and he had made the "27" into "27/10," or twenty-seven pounds and ten shillings. The farmer's right hand came out, the buyer took it, and one of the two middlemen gave a slap to their joined hands. The pigs had been sold for only ten shillings less than the farmer's asking price.

"Will you come along with us, Yank, and have a drink?" the farmer asked, smiling, and he and the middlemen and I went into the pub so miraculously handy. The buyer didn't come. He was busy. The middlemen and I ordered Guinnesses, and the farmer ordered a "club orange," a kind of pop. It wasn't until then that I observed that he was "wearing the pin." In his lapel was a small green button that means that the wearer is a member of the Pioneers. This is a total-abstinence society, and I was told that it is a matter of national honor never to ask a man wearing the pin to have a drink of liquor. Nurtured on the notion that Ireland is a place of extravagant drinking, I was amazed at the hundreds of men I saw wearing the pin. The pub, a simple one, with a bench against the wall across from the bar, was full, and the barmaid knew everyone except me. I noticed how low the voices were, as I had noticed before in pubs. I had to be careful to keep my voice under control, lest it brash out over the soft ones I heard around me. The barmaid made jokes, my friends of the moment talked local gossip, everyone drank much more slowly than we drink at home, and I felt fine, there in the town some of my people came from.

"The mother's a Yank," a man next to me said after I'd talked with him awhile and had a couple more Guinnesses.

"Born in the States, you mean?" I asked him.

"No," he said, "but she worked there for twenty-five years. I've never been there myself. The mother says it's a grand place."

"It's O.K.," I said. "In many ways, it's O.K."

After some more talk, mostly about how good the prices for pigs and cattle were, the man said, almost bashfully, "Would you have time to go with me and see the mother? She'd be greatly pleased to see someone from America. But then you'd have to be moving along, wouldn't you?"

"Tell the truth," I said, "I'm expecting my wife to come in any minute and haul me away. Is your house far from here?"

"Ah, it's only a minute or two," he said. We went around the corner and up the road a piece.

He opened a gate and we walked up to the house — a small, tidy one a few steps away — and, inside, "the mother" was sitting reading a newspaper and drinking a cup of tea. Her eyes were like those of the storyteller I met down in Kerry — gray-green. She was a tiny, neat woman, and the look in her eyes was steady, serene, and keen.

"I see Mr. Forrestal ended his life, poor man!" she said as she put down the *Irish Times*.

I was shocked. I hadn't seen the paper that day.

"And who is he?" the son asked me.

"He'd be the Minister for Defense in America, the same as Dr. O'Higgins here," the little woman explained to her son before I could answer him.

"Oh, then you two Yanks have a talk together," said the son, smiling. "I'll not bother the two of you. I don't know what you'd be talking about, the two of you."

We all had tea, and my hostess told me that she had

worked in Westchester for a long time, and we talked some more, about one thing and another.

When the visit came to an end, the son and I left the house together. As we walked to the gate, the mother stood in the doorway, and as my hand was on the gate latch, she said, "Give my fondest regards to the United States!"

I said I would.

Sometimes the thought occurred to me in Ireland that what frequently made me happy there was this: In Ireland, they do the things we used to do but don't do any more. This idea came to me when we visited a family named Walsh, near Navan, in County Meath, which is not far from Dublin. They live in a lovely Georgian house, of God knows how many rooms. "Lovely" is a word I fell into the use of in Ireland, for it is one of the most used words there. In the United States, "lovely" is a woman's word, I think; you don't hear men saying it much. That's not so in Ireland. Once, in Dublin, on a Sunday afternoon, after thousands of Dubliners had marched and sung and shouted, and speakers had made orations against the Republic of Ireland bill, then in the British Parliament, I heard a man say, "Wasn't it a lovely protest?"

Mr. and Mrs. Walsh greeted us with tea and richly buttered bread and several kinds of cake, and their two daughters, children of six and eight or so, stood courteously by, not at all ill-at-ease. Finally, Mrs. Walsh said to the smaller one, "Won't you recite for our visitors from

America?" The child made a curtsy, advanced with immeasurable poise to the center of the room, and, moving her outstretched arms as if she were a ship on the rolling sea, recited:

> I saw a ship a-sailing,
> A-sailing on the sea,
> And it was heavy-laden
> With lovely things for me.

It was so many years since I had heard anybody, child or grownup, recite anything that it was a quietly wondrous thing to hear. I suppose children still do recite things here in the States, and that probably it is because I haunt Seventy-second and Second Avenue and Madison Square Garden and Aqueduct race track and places like that that I don't get to hear them any more. At any rate, children recite in Ireland, and sweetly, too. And people take long walks, and they sit by the fire and talk without a radio going, and do all the other things we used to do but don't seem to do any more.

They had been having trouble with an electric lamp at a country house we visited in Tipperary. There appears to be something in the Irish atmosphere that makes all mechanical things work less well than they do in the air of the United States. This lamp was exasperating. Sometimes the string would have to be pulled a half-dozen times before it would light, and sometimes it wouldn't light at all. The lady of the house told us about it and about turning it over to Thomas, an old fellow who for a couple of generations had been around the demesne for the purpose of having such things turned over to him. "I'll fix it, milady," he said.

More than a week passed and the lady of the house heard nothing from Thomas.

"About that lamp, Thomas," she said to him one day when she came across him cutting the nails of one of her greyhounds. "Have you fixed it yet?"

"It's a good thing you mentioned that lamp," he said. "I've been meaning to speak to you about that lamp. I'm after studying that lamp this long while, and you'll have no more trouble with it."

"Good, Thomas!" said the lady.

"But I want to tell you," Thomas went on. "You'd want to be very careful with that lamp. If you're to have that lamp be lighting up grand for you, here's the thing. First, take a soft holt on the string. Then give it three long, slow pulls. Then one quick, little pull on it, and after that two fine, gentle, long-drawn-out pulls. Do that and you'll have no more trouble with that lamp."

Our last days in Ireland were spent at Crosshaven, which is near Cobh (pronounced "Cove," and still called Queenstown by the crew of the *Britannic,* on which we were to sail back to the United States). At odd times during those days, I recalled the dreamy notions I had had of what was ahead of us before we left East Seventy-second Street. My head had been full of all the things I had heard about Ireland from the time I was a kid, at wakes and in songs about white cottages with thatched roofs, and the smell of burning peat. (I learned within a week or so to call it turf, not peat.) After landing there and riding around the little island, only a couple of hundred miles from north to south and less than that from east to west, I always had a feeling that Ireland wasn't exactly what I had dreamed it would be. Yet it was — in a sentence or a phrase dropped by a passer-by, or timidly passed to me by a man next to me in a pub. Often I felt that these were my people, although they did not know me any more. At those times — oh, how lonely I was there! At the hotel we stayed at in Crosshaven, there was a little boy, the son of Walter Macken, the actor and writer. The father was down for a couple of weeks from the Abbey Theatre, in Dublin, to play in Cork, which is about fifteen miles from Crosshaven. The name of the little boy was Ultan. That is a name you never hear in the United States. It is pronounced "Oolthawn," with the accent on the "thawn." It is an old, old name, older than Patrick or Michael in Irish use, and to hear the little boy's mother, Peggy, say it was to hear a caress. The place where we were staying was the Bunnyconnellan Hotel, nestled on the side of a hill from which we could look out upon the splendid harbor of Cobh. Sitting on a bench in front of the hotel, in one of the bursts of sunshine that space out the rain in Ireland, the little boy and I were looking out at the sea. Ultan, who is only five, was born on the coast of Galway, where they say the sea in a rage can be a most terrifying thing. Before us, there was the empty sea, where tomorrow the ship would be. "Out there will be the *Britannic*," I said to him, "and if you look out tomorrow, you will see her. There will be no way of seeing us — it's too far to see — but we will be there, heading back to America."

Ultan walked away and plucked idly at a flower in the border of the path. Then he came back to me, the stranger he had known for only seventy hours or so. He, too, was groping, as I had long been, because he put his little hand on my arm and he said, in his beautiful Galway speech, "We'll be terribly froightened for you tomorrow whin the loiner, and you on it, starts out into the big sea."

A stranger I was, in a country I felt was my own, and a little bit of a boy, with a single sentence, ended all my groping — "We'll be terribly froightened for you tomorrow . . ."

It was our last evening in Ireland. We were staying overnight in Cork. As with all holidaymakers nearing the holiday's end, I had sorrow and eagerness blended, a sorrow that came with leaving Ireland and an eagerness to feel East Seventy-second Street again and to find out what had been going on in our neighborhood, around Maxie Slavin's newsstand, at Second. I wanted to hang on to Cork and the scenes in its streets, and at the same time hear the kids singing of a summer evening on the stoops of East Seventy-second. It couldn't be done. By telephone, the Cunard Line told us that we would have to be at the dock back in Cobh at seven o'clock in the morning, to go through the customs, board the tender, and go out to the *Britannic,* which would be at anchor in the harbor, after the overnight trip from Liverpool. That meant getting up at five and having a taxi at the hotel door at six. My wife had to do some shopping — handkerchiefs, last-minute gifts, and so on. While she did that, I dropped into the Swan and Cygnet, which is near the Old Bridge across the Lee and not far from the statue of Father Theobald Mathew, the great apostle of abstinence from liquor. In the Swan and Cygnet, one Guinness led to another, discussion of one horse race of the day led to discussion of the next, a few pleasant words were offhandedly spoken about Partition, and a few hours passed. One man quoted the *Dublin Opinion,* which had said, "Partition is like the ones landlords put up to divide houses into flats. You keep on hearing voices through it."

At nine o'clock, while it was still light in the streets from the long twilight, I was walking along thinking about those last Guinnesses and the coldness and dampness of five o'clock the next morning. In such a frame of mind I entered a wineshop, or what we would call a package store, and was greeted with a "Good evening, sir" by a tall, dignified, white-haired clerk, alone in the small shop.

"Good evening," I said. "I have something of a situation before me."

"Sit down, sir," the white-headed man said.

"I'm a visiting American," I explained.

"I thought so, sir," he said. "By the hat, you know. Bigger than ours, do you see?"

"Yes," I said. "Well, we're sailing tomorrow for America, and we have to get up at five o'clock to go down to Cobh and the dock."

"Five o'clock?" he said, unbelieving. "A shocking hour! A shocking hour! I thought we were supposed to encourage you fellows. That's no way to do it. Five o'clock in the morning! A shocking hour!"

"I'm afraid it might be cold at that hour in the morning," I went on, moving into the heart of the matter.

"It *will* be cold," he said definitely. "Where are you staying, sir?"

"At the Metropole," I answered.

"Oh, Lord!" he said. "A timperance hotel. They have no license."

"That's it," I said.

The clerk thought for a moment before he spoke. "Now," he said, "you wouldn't want to be drinking brandy at that hour of the morning, would you, sir?"

"Oh, no," I said. "That wouldn't be it."

"Tell me, sir, how long have you been in Ireland?" he asked. "Have you had time to get used to the Irish whisky?"

"Nearly a couple of months," I said. "I think the Irish whisky is all right. A little better than all right."

"Then that's fine. Irish whisky's the thing, then," he said. "Could you wait a moment, please?"

"I could," I said. "Take your time."

He went out into the stockroom and came back with a small bottle of Paddy's, an excellent brand. The bottle was of no measure familiar to me but about the size of two or three of those small bottles that are sold on American trains. The clerk held the bottle up before me and pointed to its top. It was one of those screw tops.

"Now," said the clerk, "the beauty of this is, do you see, that it can be opened without the aid of a corkscrew. Is the Missus with you?"

"She is," I said, studying the top of the bottle.

"I thought as much," he said. "Now, frequently enough the Missus does not approve of drinking at that hour of the morning, no matter how cold it is."

"You hit the nail on the head," I said.

"It's odd, but they're like that," he continued. "Well, do you understand the point I'm making about this Paddy's? The point I'm making, sir, is this. The top of this bottle may be removed *in secrecy, if necessary!*"

It was necessary, as things turned out.

2

~~~~~~

Where the Grass, They Say,
Is Blue

~~~~~~

LIKE MANY OTHER PEOPLE who have a durable fondness
for betting small sums on horse races, I have always been
quite remote from the horses themselves. Occasionally, I
do see them at the race tracks, but even then it is from
some distance. Gradually, over the years, I have been
forming the ambition to close this gap between the horses
and me. So this April I packed a bag and went down to
the Blue Grass region of Kentucky, the heart of the horse
country, to visit for a couple of weeks. I chose April because more race horses are born in that month than in
any other. Since my aim was to make the personal acquaintance of the runners, I might as well begin at the
beginning, I thought.

Animals were to be the focal point of this holiday, and,

by chance, an animal became the topic of talk on my train journey to Lexington, Kentucky. It was not, however, a horse but a chimpanzee — a chimpanzee of uncommon aptitudes. The train, the George Washington, had just sauntered into the State of Kentucky when I found myself in the smoking compartment listening to the conductor, who had no duties to perform at the moment. It is noticeable that tongues are loosened by the vibration of trains, and the conductor was chummily conversational. "I've been on this train, Number One, for years," he said. "Funny things happen on it. Like the time the fellow I took over from for the night run, another conductor, never told me anything about what was in the baggage car. Never said a word. I went into the baggage car to sit down and eat my lunch that I always bring from home. Well, sir, I was sitting there eating the lunch and all of a sudden I looked down and there's a kind of a big chimpanzee sitting beside the crate I was on. He was looking up at me as calm and as natural as you please. About four feet tall, he was. Very quiet. Sitting there watching me eat. By that time, I had reached what you might call the dessert course, and I was eating a banana. This damn ape could almost talk. I wasn't the least bit afraid of him. He practically told me, the way he looked at me, that he could use a little lunch, too. So I handed him another banana I had, and he sat there and peeled it and ate it exactly the way he saw me do it. The two of us sat there like old buddies, having our lunch in the dead of the night. I had a cup of tea and poured him one, in a paper cup.

He held the paper cup of tea without squashing it
and he looked up between sips like he was thanking
me.

"We finished our lunch, me and the ape, and I still
had nothing to do. Some baggage cars got iron bars running along the walls. For fun, I went over and began
grabbing the bars on the wall, walking the length of
the car grabbing one bar after another. I used to see
monkeys swinging from bars in the zoo up at Cincinnati,
and I wondered if he'd get the idea. He sure did get it.
I unloosened the leash around his neck, and, sure as
you're born, over he went — jumped up and grabbed a
bar on the wall. In a jiffy, he went swinging down from
one end of the car to the other, never touching the floor.
I swear to God it was just like he was saying, 'If this is
what you're trying to do, old man, here's the way to do
it. You're doing it like a rank amateur.'

"He was a family pet of some rich New Yorkers that
were passengers. They were taking him to Hot Springs
with them. I had to go back through the train once in a
while, doing my work. I'd fasten the leash each time
I left and unfasten it when I came back. Each time, the
monk would show me how to swing on bars. He seemed
very disappointed that I didn't catch on to the trick and
go galumphing along the wall like him.

"Him and me had a very pleasant night in the baggage car. At odd times that night, I got the notion that
I was showing him how to be a man, like showing him
how to eat, and at the same time he was showing
me how to be a chimpanzee, like showing me how to

swing on bars. Neither one of us made much head-
way winning the other over, but it made quite a
night."

Any man who lives on East Seventy-second Street, as
I do, has a black curse on him if he is habitually unable
to sleep after five-thirty or six o'clock in the morning, because this is an unusual affliction in the city and the man
is therefore bound to be lonesome by seven o'clock, since
he has nobody to talk to. In Lexington, however, a man
finds early rising a pleasure. As a chronic early riser, I
certainly found my first morning in Lexington to be just
that. I was stopping at the Lafayette Hotel. Up at five-
thirty, I dressed and went down to the lobby, where a
large oil painting of Sweep, the famed race horse and
sire, hangs over the reception desk. In fact, paintings of
horses adorn every wall in the Lafayette lobby. It seems
a fitting *décor,* because Lexington has no other industry
to compete in size and interest with the business of breeding, raising, racing, and selling Thoroughbreds. (So re-
spected is the running horse in the Blue Grass region
that "thoroughbred" is invariably spelled there with a
capital "T.") That first morning, I found three Kentucky horsemen seated under a blown-up photograph of
a fiery stallion, the great Bull Dog. The men had presumably breakfasted, although it was not yet six, and had
already begun their day's chatting. It was about horses
and kindred subjects, naturally. All three men were in
their sixties, surely, and obviously healthier than many a
twenty-year-old. Their complexions were brown, clean,

and seasoned; the texture of their skin made me think that they had washed every day for years with saddle soap. They had keen eyes, with wrinkles around them, no doubt the result of their having laughed a lot in their time, and of their having squinted a lot as they peered across broad country paddocks or into the distant reaches of race tracks. I could not resist sitting within eavesdropping distance of them for a few minutes before going out for my coffee. (The dining room doesn't open until the leisurely hour of 7 A.M.)

"Man alive, grass is the most important thing in the world!" one of the men said. "Ain't nothing anywheres near as important as grass, Jody."

"Maybe," the man called Jody answered. "But I can't eat it. No, Jud, I can't eat it."

"Course you can't eat it," Jud said. "Neb'ch'nezzar in the Bible got down and started nibbling on it and they damn near put him away for doing it. Just the same, Jody, grass is pretty important to you. Ever stop to think what a cow is, Jody?"

"What's cows got to do with it?" Jody asked. "We're talking horses, ain't we?"

"Let me tell you something, Jody," Jud said. "A cow ain't nothing but a machine that makes you and me able to eat grass. That's an idea stuck in my craw ever since I read it somewheres. You can't eat grass. All right, a cow can eat grass, and plenty of it. So the cow eats the grass and turns it into beef and turns it into milk, and we eat the beef and we drink the milk, don't we? Cow ain't nothing but a machine that makes grass fit for us people to eat. Listen to me, Jody, and you're bound to learn something every day."

"All I just learnt is cows eat grass and I eat meat," said Jody. "I knew that long ago."

"I'm proving to you grass is the most important thing in the world," Jud said.

"Mightn't be most important in the whole world," Jody said, "but Lexington, Kentucky, sure would be in one hell of a fix without it. That I *do* know."

Later that morning, I went out to the Coldstream Stud Farm, which is a few miles from Lexington, on New-town Pike. Coldstream was the main objective of my trip. Before leaving New York, I had arranged to spend most of my time there. One of the first subjects I took up with Charles A. Kenney, Coldstream's manager, was grass, and especially Kentucky grass.

"The Blue Grass country really consists of a thirty- or thirty-five-mile circle centering around Lexington," Mr. Kenney told me. "We figure it's the best grass there is for raising Thoroughbreds, or any other kind of horse. Suitable to their stomachs and the ground is full of lime-stone, which puts calcium in the grass and makes good bones. 'Got more vitamins in it than you can shake a stick at, too."

"It looks thoroughly green to me," I said. "I've often wondered why they call it blue grass. Now that I'm walk-ing through it, I wonder all the more."

"Everybody does, including me," said my host. "And I've been looking at it all my life. They do say, though, that a certain time of summer, when there's a kind of tiny, pinhead-size blossom on it, there's a bluish tinge to it. That is, if the wind is blowing it at just the right angle and the sunlight is striking it just exactly right. Between the two of us, it always looks mighty green to me, except when it's brown in the late fall and winter. You've got to have special Kentucky eyes to see it blue, and I reckon I haven't got them."

As we walked around that morning, getting a preliminary view of Coldstream, Mr. Kenney told me a few things about himself and the place. He is a tall, strongly built man, of pleasant manner and wide vocabulary, with an easy courtesy in his friendliness — a gift I later found not at all exceptional in the Blue Grass country. Mr. Kenney was born forty-eight years ago in Paris, which is in Bourbon County, about eighteen miles from Lexington. (The prevalence of French place names is conspicuous in this region. The town of Versailles — pronounced "Versales" — is only a short distance from Lexington.) Coldstream is owned by a man in his early thirties — the only man I met in Kentucky who can sport four initials. He is Elmer Ellsworth Dale Shaffer — pronounced "Shay-fer" — and the farm was left to him by his father, a Pennsylvanian who made his fortune in gas and oil in the West. Coldstream is about nine hundred acres, on which there are no fewer than eight barns; the farm is divided into dozens of fenced fields, or paddocks, each serving a specific purpose in the plan of operation, which calls for, among other things, raising thirty-five to forty baby race horses every year. These, of course, are in addition to the yearlings — "last year's crop," they are called — and the mares, numbering forty-five or so, and the six or eight stallions that constitute the rest of the farm's Thoroughbred population. Then, too, there is a herd of Aberdeen Angus cattle. "It's good stock but doesn't pretend to be prize stock," Mr. Kenney said. At the time of my visit, the herd numbered exactly a hundred. "And, oh, yes, I almost forgot," he said. "We also raise about two hundred turkeys every year. We give most of those away at Christmas to friends, from one end of the country to the other." In the world of horses, "from one end of the country to the other" means from Santa Anita, in California, to Belmont Park, in New York, to Hialeah Park, in Florida, with all the eighty or ninety race tracks in between.

A breeding farm the size of Coldstream costs between $250,000 and $300,000 a year to operate. It is not nearly the largest farm of its kind in the Blue Grass, but, as I gathered from various people during my visit, it is a farm with an enviable reputation. Its live produce is of the best, I was told by Kentuckians, and in support of this, they pointed out that last year Coldstream sold seventeen yearlings at public auction for a total of $228,208. The average price was $13,424, one of the highest averages in the country. Unlike certain other breeding farms, some of them larger, Coldstream is a paying proposition. Some of the others are rich men's pastimes, operating at annual losses of a half million or more. Coldstream has not always run a racing stable, but nowadays it does. It races nothing but fillies, and is the only stable of its size in the country to do so.

One thing that I was determined to see while I was in Kentucky was the very earliest hours in the life of a race horse, and I told Mr. Kenney so.

"That's not too much to ask," he said, "even if these mares don't always co-operate with us in the matter of foaling. Most foals are born during the night — did you know that?"

"No," I said. "I don't know anything about it, tell the truth."

"Well, it's so," Mr. Kenney said. "I've often thought about that fact, and I reckon it's something that goes back centuries and centuries — thousands of centuries. As far back, maybe, as when a horse was an Eohippus and was only about eleven inches high. It was advantageous to give birth in the dark of the night, I figure, because then the mare's enemies wouldn't have so much chance of catching her and her baby at a bad time."

"That could be," I said.

"Anyway," he said, "Herbert Barnes, our foaling man, will let us know about the mare we have closest to foaling time. That's Fille d'Orlean. She's an American mare, but several of her ancestors had French names. And, by the way, that Orlean is spelled without an 's' on it. Ought to have an 's,' but, as you probably know, the rules for naming race horses allow only fourteen characters and spaces in a name, so we chopped the 's' off."

"Well, how soon is she going to have a foal?" I asked.

"Any time now," Mr. Kenney replied. "The sire is

Goya II, a pretty famous French horse. We have good hopes for this foal. Hope he's a colt."

That very night, at the Lafayette, I got a phone call from Mr. Kenney. It was about ten-thirty. "The foaling man just phoned me to come over," he said. "That mare's about ready to have her foal, he says. I'll come into town and pick you up, if you'd like." I told him I'd wait for him in the lobby.

As Mr. Kenney and I rode out along Newtown Pike through the quiet night, there wasn't much talk. We were taking in the lovely cleanliness of the miles of white fences, immaculate stripes against the darkness of the fields beyond. I looked at them happily as a stranger, Mr. Kenney with the familiar liking for a land he had known all his life. (Those white fences are a badge of the Blue Grass region. Later on, I was told that one farm, Calumet, spends at least thirty thousand dollars a year on painting alone, to pridefully maintain the beauty, as well as the usefulness, of fences and barns.) And as we rode the four miles or so to Coldstream, I mused on how far this experience — a nighttime ride to be present at the birth of a racer who, at best, will not be seen at the tracks until 1952 — was from standing out of the rain in a doorway on Second Avenue conferring somewhat stealthily with a bookmaker over a two-buck bet on Mangohick in the fourth at Belmont.

One of the barns at Coldstream is a foaling barn, and it was brightly lighted when we arrived. Ordinarily, it is lighted only dimly at night; on this occasion, it had a festive brilliance — the kind one might imagine a castle would have on the night a royal heir is to be born. "Let's go inside and see the foaling man," Mr. Kenney said as we got out of his car. A big red dog named Coldstream greeted us at the door of the barn. When we reached the stall of Fille d'Orlean, on the half door of which was a typewritten card bearing her name — along with Goya II's — Mr. Kenney glanced in, then turned to me and said, "Look!" Over the half door I had my first sight of a newborn Thoroughbred.

"It's a colt, Mr. Kenney, sir," said Mr. Barnes, the foaling man, who was standing with watchful and kindly eyes in a corner of the big stall, ankle deep in straw.

"Just how old is he now?" I asked.

"Let me see," said Mr. Barnes, taking a thick, old-fashioned gold watch out of a pocket of his white jumper. "Now it's eleven-forty-two. He was foaled at eleven-thirty. He's twelve minutes old. Fine, big colt, isn't he?"

The baby was lying in the deep straw, close to his mother, who was also lying down. To me, he looked strikingly beautiful — never mind the gauntness of his body, the incredibly stiltlike legs. He seemed all legs, face, and eyes. He was lying where his mother, without rising or even moving very much, could turn her head, stick out her tongue, and lick his face and neck, smoothing down his coat, which was awry.

"At this point," Mr. Kenney said, smiling, "I often wonder if the mother knew ahead of time what it was all about. Or does the whole thing come as a delightful surprise?"

The colt looked inquisitive but sleepy. In answer to my questions, Mr. Barnes said that the birth had been an easy one, both for the mare and for him. "I didn't need to help her hardly at all," he said. "I'm waiting now for the colt to get up. Often, they're on their feet before this — sometimes less than ten minutes after they're born. Usually fall down the first time they try it, but they make another try at it in a couple of minutes. Second try, they usually make it."

I had never seen Fille d'Orlean race, but while keeping her company there in front of the stall, I could well imagine her — sleek, shiny, keyed-up, in racing trim — as she must have looked mincing to the post. Now she was before us in the far different role of mother. She was tired, fat, still weak, and serenely full of concern for the small colt leggily sprawled so near her, close enough to feel the warmth of her breath and her caressing, reassuring tongue.

The baby was forty minutes old before he decided to try to get on his feet. At ten minutes after midnight, we watched him most awkwardly unlimber those bony, disobedient forelegs and plant two small, perfectly formed hoofs on the floor. Then we saw him adventurously arrange the two rear hoofs in similar manner and get up. For an instant, he wavered. But he was for that instant triumphantly on his pins, in brave ridiculousness. Then he tumbled into the straw, unhurt, and our friendly laughter was one of the first sounds he heard in the big world.

A minute or two passed, and then he was up again.

It was amazing, the skill he had acquired in his single previous try. This time, he stayed up, looking around him cautiously to be certain that the process of getting up had not removed him too far from that warm, protective body of which he had been a part only an hour before. The colt remained standing for ten minutes or more, once in a while taking a few tentative steps around the stall, nearly always with an eye on his mother.

"How much do they weigh, as a rule?" I asked Mr. Kenney.

"I don't know," he answered. "How much does a foal weigh, Barnes?"

"Mr. Kenney, sir, I don't know either," the foaling man answered. "Never have weighed a foal, and I've been a foaling man for more than twenty-five years. Too much else to do at this stage of the game to fool around weighing 'em."

The newborn son of Goya II and Fille d'Orlean seemed to grow handsomer as he moved around. Awkward though he was, there was a graceful flow to his movements. He was a fine, healthy colt, and his color was a sort of tawny chestnut. Down the center of his face was a broad white streak — a blaze, it's called. The white terminated in a point, distinctly decorative, between his nostrils, which were wide. I made a remark about the blaze.

Mr. Kenney had been sizing up, with expert eye, every feature of the colt, and seemed more than satisfied with his appearance. "That's good, those big nostrils," he told me. "They can scoop up plenty of air. A day will come

when this little fellow will be racing down the stretch —
I hope — and he'll need plenty of air in his lungs. Let's
go and have some coffee."

As we started off for a small room farther down the
barn, from which came the smell of fresh coffee cutting
through the unforgettable odors of a racing barn — hay,
medicine, ammonia, the sweat of animals — the little colt
lay down. I glanced back at him, and his eyes were
closed as if he were going to sleep. He'd been up and
around, and, after all, there wasn't much to see in a
world made up of just one stall.

At six the next morning, when I went down to the
lobby of the Lafayette, the three mellow horsemen were
again in their cozy corner. What was more noteworthy,
they were again, or possibly still, talking grass. This time,
it was the one called Jody who was holding forth, and the
long-talking Jud was listening.

"Limestone, limestone, limestone!" said Jody petu-
lantly. "I'm sick and tired of hearing about limestone in
the grass. Dammit, if they was nothing in the grass but
this here limestone, the stuff would be white. Wouldn't
be green, or blue, or yellow with pink polka dots, or anything else. It'd be white."

"There's other things in it besides limestone," Jud said,
with surprising meekness.

"But all you hear about is the dammed limestone," Jody
asserted. "For me, I figure they must be plenty of limestone in the water, and it's the water around here that
makes the bourbon so good. So I figure I'll get my

share of limestone in the whisky. Best way to get it."

"Listen, Jody," said Jud. "You said at breakfast you weren't feeling so good this morning. And I noticed you were giving that bourbon a good going over yesterday."

"Now, now!" Jody said. "It wasn't the bourbon made me feel a little off-color this morning. I know what happened to me. What I done last night is run into a batch of stale ice cubes. That's what done it, stale ice cubes."

At breakfast, I kept thinking back to Mr. Kenney's remark that nearly all foals are born during the nighttime. It had not taken long in Lexington to learn that when a person there is wondering about any facts or statistics having to do with Thoroughbreds, the thing to do is go and ask Mr. J. A. Estes. Of Mr. Estes, a scholarly graduate of the University of Kentucky and now contributing editor and research director of the *Blood-Horse,* a learned magazine published weekly in Lexington, a Kentucky acquaintance had said to me, "I honestly believe that if you went up to Joe Estes and asked him how many bay horses with three white feet had won six-furlong races on Thursday afternoons during 1934, he wouldn't blink an eye but would give you an answer without even looking it up." So I was not in the least astonished at the readiness of Mr. Estes's reply when I went to his office and asked him about the hours when foals are born. "It so happens that I made a study of that back in 1935," he said. "We'll look it up in the magazine." The Estes study covered the birth of three hundred and seventy-six foals. The figures showed that the vast majority of these

were born during what Mr. Estes calls the "dark hours";
that is, between 6 P.M. and 6 A.M. "To be exact," said
the great figure man, "of the foals I tabulated, 83.22 per
cent were born in that period. Between 7 P.M. and midnight, 55.7 per cent were born. The peak hour was between 9 P.M. and 10 P.M., for which the figure is 13.03
per cent. The smallest number were born between noon
and 6 P.M. None of the 376 was born during the hour
between 2 P.M. and 3 P.M. That answer the question?"

"It does," I said, and immediately I wondered if a
similar study had been made of human babies. Later, I
found that of a thousand children tabulated at the
Chicago Lying-In Hospital, five hundred and seven
babies were born during the "dark hours." That is, of
course, 50.7 per cent. And it was revealed that, just as
with the horses, the smallest number of babies were born
between noon and 6 P.M. What all this proves, I haven't
the slightest idea.

Out at Coldstream at ten o'clock that same morning,
it was a delight to look into the paddock next to the foaling barn and see Fille d'Orlean and her foal walking
around as big as life. The colt was now only ten and a
half hours old. Yet there he was dutifully following his
mother around the field, nuzzling her to get something
to eat whenever he thought of it, which was often. He
was never more than three or four feet away from her,
and every once in a while, between snacks, he would
move up beside her and rub his downy nose against her
muzzle.

"Does she know him from any other foal who might be around?" I asked Mr. Kenney, who had joined me at the paddock fence, his morning's work finished.

"For today, she probably does, by the smell," he answered. "But in a couple of days she probably won't know him from any other foal. They're kind of dumb that way. The foal knows his own mother, though, as long as he's getting milk from her."

Mr. Kenney and I got into his car and drove over to the stallions' paddock. There are seven stallions on the farm now, four of them wholly owned by Coldstream, and the others either the property of syndicates in which Mr. Shaffer is a member or owned by friends of his. "There's the greatest of them all," Mr. Kenney said soon after we reached the paddock. He pointed to a big, dark horse. "That's our Bull Dog. His hundred and ninety-five sons and daughters had won $4,964,564 at the end of 1949. Bull Dog's twenty-three years old. He's retired from the stud now. Finished a couple of years ago. I don't need to tell you he's the sire of Bull Lea, and Bull Lea is Citation's pappy."

The active sires owned by Coldstream are Heliopolis, fourteen years old (very likely the most valuable animal on the farm; reportedly, there have been offers nearing a half million for him); Reaping Reward, sixteen; and Coldstream, seventeen. Mr. Kenney told me that a large part of the farm's revenue comes from the stud fees earned by these stallions. In 1949, Heliopolis served twenty-two outside mares, at $1,500 each. That year, Reaping Reward served thirty-two outside mares, at

$1,000. The fee for Bull Dog was $2,500 when he was at his peak. "And Coldstream," Mr. Kenney said, "well, he's considered a desirable sire, but by nature he's a shy fellow, and he had only thirteen outside mares last year, at five hundred dollars. We sold one of his sons a few years ago for fifty thousand dollars. That was Royal Blood, whose mother was Spotted Beauty. She was a daughter of Man o' War."

Early one morning a couple of days afterward, Mr. Kenney and I were walking across the paddock next to the foaling barn when my attention was caught by something about fifty yards away. "Hold everything, Mr. Kenney!" I said, and took him by the arm. "I think I've got it! Look over there! See that patch just this side of the big tree? The sun's hitting it exactly right and there's enough of a breeze to bend it a little. That's blue grass, all right! Now I can understand the name. I must be getting to be a Kentuckian. I can see the blue grass now."

"You sure are learning fast," he said. "That's onions! One of the most unwelcome things we got, a patch of wild onions. Always sprouting up right in the middle of a nice field of grass."

"Oh," I said. "Hard to get rid of, is that it?"

"Old Kentucky man told me once that there was only one way to get shet of wild onions," Mr. Kenney said. "When I asked him what it was, he said, 'You die and leave 'em, that's all.'"

*　　*　　*

On my last day in Kentucky, Mr. Kenney, for reasons best known to himself, had to take two mares out of one paddock and lead them to another, and I accompanied him. As we were driving over to their paddock, he stopped at a barn and got a quart bucket of oats, which, he explained, would make it easier for us to get the mares to come over to us. Then he went on to the paddock. There was no need of the oats to lure one animal over. She came ambling across the field while we still sat in the car. The door of the car was open, and the mare came up, stuck her head in, and looked around inside, bold but friendly.

"That's the famous Miss Mommy," Mr. Kenney said. "Good mare. They named her after Mrs. Shaffer. Children around Coldstream call Mrs. Shaffer Miss Mommy."

We got out, and Mr. Kenney put a leather lead on Miss Mommy and told me to hold her while he took the oats and walked over to lure the second mare. When he came back with her on a lead, I asked him who she was.

"This is Be Faithful," he said. "A pretty costly girl. Mr. Shaffer paid Louis B. Mayer a hundred thousand dollars for her in 1946. She was a great racer. She won about eighty-eight thousand dollars for us at the races the very next year. She's eight years old now. Here, take the oats. You can lead Miss Mommy. Give her some of the oats. Be Faithful has had her share."

I held the lead in my right hand and walked uneasily along with the famed and amiable Miss Mommy. I was on her left, holding the bucket in my left hand and letting Miss Mommy have a few nibbles of oats as we

walked. Be Faithful was on my left, and on *her* left was
Mr. Kenney. Be Faithful wanted some oats, and she
reached over for them. I turned my head toward her and,
with my elbow, tried to nudge her away from the oats.
At the same time, Miss Mommy decided to take the
matter of oats into her own hands. She began trying to
jerk the lead out of my hand and, turning, kicked out
at Be Faithful with both hind legs. She missed Be Faithful, but she landed on me. The kick struck me precisely
where kicks are supposed to strike. Be Faithful started
kicking back, and I was between the two of them. Oats
and lead flew out of my hands, and I made for a tree on
the edge of the field.

Safely behind the tree, I tried to catch my breath.
Mr. Kenney had the situation in hand. He had skillfully
separated the two mares and grabbed Miss Mommy's
lead. "You made that furlong in nine and a fifth seconds!" he hollered over.

The kick didn't hurt, really. It did me no harm phys-
ically. And spiritually, I've been thinking, it did me a lot
of good. Excellent for the ego. How many other two-
dollar horse players around East Seventy-second Street
will ever be in a position to say that they have been
kicked in the pants by Miss Mommy?

3

∿∿∿

Bellevue Days

∿∿∿

ONE AFTERNOON RECENTLY, after visiting friends on Gramercy Park, I took a cab to go to East Seventy-second Street, where I live, and the driver chose to go up First Avenue. We were halted by a light at Twenty-sixth Street, in front of Bellevue Hospital. While we waited, both the driver and I looked at the big, dull buildings and the many yards, and watched the flow of people through the gates.

"Good old Bellevue!" I said.

"My wife's brother was in there once," the driver said before the light changed and we started on our way again. "He had what they call a sacroiliac, a very painful thing in the back. It must be a tough spot to be in, that Bellevue."

"I was in there once, too," I said.

"No kidding?" the driver asked.

"No kidding," I said. "And you're right. It is kind of tough in there sometimes. But just the same, I've got a soft spot in my heart for old Bellevue."

"What was it — accident or something?" the driver asked.

"No," I said. "Heart attack. But I'm practically O.K. now. That was a couple of years ago."

"You got to take it easy if you've had one of those," he said.

"They made me take it easy in Bellevue," I said. "And I want to tell you I met some fine people in there and they all certainly treated me first-rate."

"Now, that's a funny thing," said the driver. "My wife's brother said almost the same words many a time. Said he met some fine people in there, and the treatment he got from everybody was real good. Almost the same words you said."

When I got home that afternoon, it turned out that my wife was still out shopping, so I made myself a cup of tea and sat down to rest for a while, as I often do these days. I had to laugh a little to myself at the idea of having said "Good old Bellevue!" to a stranger. Yet that is the way I feel whenever I chance to pass the place — almost as if it were some school I attended as a youth and could not let slip lightly from my mind. Indeed, it *was* almost that way — like an alma mater.

*   *   *

In the middle of May, 1947, our flat was being painted (for the first time in three years), and the place was a mess. My wife thought it would be a good opportunity to visit her mother, in Wakefield, Rhode Island. As for me, I had some work to do in town, and I also liked to go to the races at Belmont in the afternoon, when my work was through. So she went to the country, and I moved into an inexpensive room in a hotel in East Fortieth Street, near Lexington.

The night of May 22nd (I remember the dates well, because they have been on so many records since then) I had dinner alone — a steak and au gratin potatoes, with a drink before dinner and a bottle of beer with it. After dinner, it then being about ten o'clock, I bought the *Daily Racing Form* at Forty-second Street and Third Avenue, from a blind man, and walked to the hotel. Before I went up to my room on the fourth floor, I stopped at the desk to chat with Louis Schwartz, the night clerk, who was there early. He and I had struck up a friendship, based on the fact that we both were horse players. He had noticed me coming in nightly with the *Form* tucked under my arm, and one word had led to another until we found out that we were both "watching" the same horse, as horse players say. That is, we were both looking every day for a particular horse's name in the entries, and sometimes bet on him when he did run. The name of the horse we both happened to have singled out was *Deep Texas*. He was a pretty good sort of horse. He never got famous, but it is safe to say that thousands of horse players throughout the country were at that time "watching" *Deep Texas.* He won a few times, too.

"Our horse isn't going tomorrow," Louis said as he gave me my room key.

"No, I already looked," I said. "Well, I'll give you a ring if I see anything. I'm going upstairs and look them over."

"Good night," Louis said. "Ring me down here if you see anything you like for tomorrow. I drop four bucks today."

"Tomorrow's another day," I said, using a practically compulsory rejoinder among horse players.

No matter how much a man likes his own home, a week or so by himself in a hotel room can be pretty nice, every year or so. I found it pleasant that night. To come into the small but comfortable room, nicely tidied up after I had left it in disarray, was pleasing, and the room's very smallness made things handy and matters manageable. Everything going fine, I thought, as I opened the window, fixed the bed light at the proper angle, and got into bed with the *Form.* For a moment, I considered spending seventy-five cents in calling my wife in Rhode Island, but then I decided that I didn't have seventy-five cents' worth of anything to say to her, except to tell her I was comfortable and ask if she was the same. I dismissed the notion and looked over nearly all the entries for the next day's racing. It seemed to be a most ordinary card, and there was no horse I had any great conviction about, so I let the *Form* drop to the floor, turned out the light, and went to sleep in two shakes of a lamb's tail. Didn't even have to count the shakes.

I awoke about six the next morning, too early for coffee to be sent up, so I figured I'd get shaved and dressed and go over to the Shack at Forty-first and Lexington for some coffee, and read the papers there. I changed from pajamas into underwear and started to shave. In the middle of that job, a pain came into the center of my chest. It was not a startling pain, not a dreadful one at all, just such a pain as anyone might have, but I thought I might lie down for a few minutes. Some little passing jiggeroo of the system, I told myself. After a while, when it didn't go away, I thought I might call Louis downstairs, for comfort and reassurance if for nothing else. I was glad I knew Louis, and that he was not just any old hotel clerk. I wouldn't have wanted to call any old hotel clerk if this little mishap turned out to be nothing at all, but with my horse-playing friend it would be all right to call anyway. I picked up the phone and waited until Louis answered. He handled the switchboard as well as the desk at that hour.

"Louis," I said, "I didn't see anything good in the entries, so I didn't call last night. But listen, Louis, I think I'm getting sick."

"What's the matter?" he asked.

"Well, I don't know, but could you come up? I'm not kidding, I'm feeling pretty sick," I said.

"You sound scared," he said. "Don't get scared. It'll only take me a couple of minutes. I'll put the elevator guy on the desk here and run the car myself. I'll be right up."

That smart Louis must have had a key with him, because he let himself in without making me come to the door. I said hello to him, and he said, "Geez, you don't look good. I think you better be quiet. There's a doctor lives upstairs. I'll run up and get him. Take it easy, now. I'll be right back." He was back in a very short time, but in that short interval I was thinking I might be making a hullabaloo over nothing. The doctor who came in with Louis was a jaunty fellow, wearing an undershirt, pants, and slippers. Because he was jaunty, I grinned rather foolishly at him, and started to sit up in bed. "Lie down," he said. "Lie still. What's the trouble?" He took my pulse and listened to my chest. He had no stethoscope — just put his head down and listened to my heartbeat. "Keep as quiet as you can," he said to me, and then spoke to Louis. "Call the cops," he said to him. "Don't try to get him into any fancy hospital. Tell the cops to get an ambulance here from Bellevue right away."

Louis went out, and again I foolishly tried to grin at the doctor. He didn't grin back, he was very calm and on-the-level-looking. "You're having a heart attack," he said. "Don't move around at all." He took a vial from his pants' pocket, shook out two pills, and gave them to me, telling me to swallow them. "I'll get you some water," he said. "Lie still. They'll be here and take care of you. Don't get frightened, old boy."

Soon a white-coated interne and two young cops carrying a stretcher came in with Louis. The doctor talked with the interne in the bathroom, and one of the young cops said to me, most sympathetically, "Take it easy, Mac." (He didn't know that "Mac" was right for my nickname; he probably called everyone that.)

"*You* fellows take it easy," I said. "I'm going to be all right."

"Sure, Mac," the cop said.

"Here's your pants and shirt," Louis said to me. "Put them on nice and easy. I got your topcoat and your other things."

The interne told me to lie down on the stretcher, and I did. Before I had got used to the feeling of being carried, I was lifted gently and skillfully into the ambulance. The siren began to whine, and the ambulance swung around the corner of Lexington and headed south.

Although I was lying down in the ambulance and unable to see out, I could sense pleasurably that it was a fine, bright morning. My apprehension of a few minutes before was inexplicably gone, perhaps only momentarily, but gone. I kept thinking how many times I had heard ambulances sounding in the streets of New York and had paid small attention. This time, it was me who was in the ambulance, with its siren whining away at seven o'clock or so of a May morning. This time, I was the one, out of eight million people, who had suddenly been taken sick. A night clerk, a casual doctor (whose name I still don't know), two young cops, an interne, and an ambulance driver were all pitching in to help the sick man. They didn't know who he was, never saw him before, didn't give a damn, particularly. Man alive, but this is a great town, I was thinking as the ambulance slowed down, went through some gates, and stopped at an entrance, where they lifted me out on the stretcher and carried me into Bellevue. I had heard and read about Bellevue all my life, but I had never been in there before.

Inside the hospital, my anxiety returned. It seemed to me, lying on one of those wheeled tables, that they were asking a vast number of questions before anything was done. Name and address, of course, and age, which was fifty-one, and previous illnesses, of which there had been practically none. Dozens of other statistics, too, it seemed. I answered as best I could, and then I was taken to an elevator and up to a ward. The ward, I heard a man say in the elevator, was B-1. The table I was on was wheeled along between the long rows of beds, so close together, and when it reached the bed I was to occupy, down near the end, I started to rise, to climb into bed.

"Hey!" the attendant shouted at me with authority. "Don't you move an inch." A big, strong fellow, he lifted me into the bed in a jiffy. "What time is it?" I asked him.

"The time doesn't make any difference, pal," he said. "It's about twenty-five past seven." That's really pretty good, I thought to myself. Only about an hour since this hit me, and here I am in bed in Bellevue already. Two nurses were by my bed, and they put a screen around it. But before they had done so, I had time to notice men in bathrobes, walking patients, strolling by. Each one looked intently at me for an instant, studying the new man just brought in, the new member of the ward. These passers-by did not stop; they merely looked, in a studious way, and then continued on to stand, with great idleness, looking out the big, arched window at the end of the ward, through which I could see the East River. Tugboats were coming prettily down the river, but in a moment the nurses and their screen blocked all that from view.

Soon, two doctors, both young, were with me, doing things with stethoscopes and, in a kindly but swift manner, asking questions. Dozens of times, from the doctors and the nurses, and even once from a passing bathrobed man, I heard the great admonition of our town, "Take it easy, now." The doctors gave me some medicine, and I lay back on the pillow, taking it easy between trying to get squints at the East River, and then I fell asleep.

The great joke among us men in Ward B-1, for all the twenty-six days I was there, was to call the place the Vitamin Ward, on account of B-1 being a famous vitamin. It was a simple joke, but we all liked it, no matter how many times it was pulled. The Vitamin Ward contained mostly heart cases and pulmonary cases, but there were a few strays of other kinds. The capacity of the ward was thirty-four, and beds were seldom empty more than a few hours.

About the first fellow I became acquainted with was a big man — Princeton 1911, it turned out — who looked like an American version of the traditional British sergeant major. He had a whopper of a mustache, and walked around in his pajamas and bathrobe as if he were about to shake up the troops for regimental inspection. Also on the roster of our ward was Alfred the Armenian, a horse player on the outside, like me, who was permanently distressed because he had been saving up betting money all winter and then had wound up in Bellevue exactly on the day in April when the New York racing season opened, at Jamaica. And there was Olsen, a thirty-five-year-old baseball fan who seemed unable to keep from catching pneumonia; he'd been in and out of Bellevue for four or five years, pneumonia having caught him five times in that period. And there were a few others who, as the days passed, changed in my mind from units in a parade of washed-out bathrobes and pajamas into individual persons I knew.

Those bathrobes at Bellevue are honeys. They're curiously pink or purplish-gray, and they've been washed a thousand times, and so have the pajamas. Nearly everyone lying in bed and looking at them go by, with people in them, has the commonplace thought that if the president of U. S. Steel and a scratch bum from a doorway were dressed in that Bellevue rig, it would be all even between them. Great levelers, those bathrobes. Most of the time, as I said, there were thirty-four of us in Ward B-1. Not all of us were stony-broke, but some were. Most were. That didn't make a particle of difference. All thirty-four of us were on the side lines of the city for as long as we were in B-1. Before we got there and after we got out again, we had done and would again do different things to get by. One of us would be a dishwasher once more, as Alfred the Armenian had been. Another would push a hack around Brooklyn, the way Milton, who was three beds up from me, did. No matter what it was we had done or would do for a living, for the time it was all even among us. Whatever was going on outside the windows, in the city of New York, we had no part of it. We didn't even have any part in the affairs of our families, if we had any. Some didn't have any. Perhaps that sounds dismal, but it wasn't. There was a kind of serenity to it.

There was a man died in the bed next to me one night, and I think that to him it was like going through a door he didn't want to go through. He came in during the afternoon, and after the doctor talked to him and those who had brought him, I talked to the doctor about my new neighbor. "He's too late," the doctor said. The new man was gaunt and sepulchral. Later in the afternoon, his folks came in to see him. They sat, a woman and a young girl, whom I presumed to be his wife and daughter, in the narrow space between our beds. When families visit in Bellevue, they often have nothing to say. They sit in that space between the beds, and maybe once in a while the wife of the sick man touches his arm and strokes it, but stops quickly because she is a little ashamed, it being so public a place. They speak a few words and then sit silently, and the sons and daughters usually look around at the other people more than they look at their father. There seems to be nothing the family can say, except to answer the sick man, who generally asks only the simplest questions, like "How is Willie?"

The gaunt man's folks left about six o'clock, and after that he lay in bed staring around a lot but not saying anything. Before the night came down and the dimmed ward lights went on, he began to talk. I couldn't understand the words, but I could see his eyes, and they were looking at me, because I was the nearest person to him. Later — it must have been two or three o'clock — he began to holler.

"Hey!" someone in the semi-darkness down the ward shouted. "Shut up! We got to sleep. Shut up, pal!" The man didn't hear him, I guess. If he did, he kept on talking anyway. There was enough light for me to see him. He stretched out a bony arm toward me and said, "Hold me, hold me, somebody, I die." He wanted somebody to take his hand and keep him this side of the door. "Hold me, hold me, somebody, I die!" he hollered, loud this time, and he tried to get up. "Shut up," another voice down the ward said.

"Listen," I said to him. "Nobody who can yell as loud as you is going to die."

"Hold me somebody," he said persistently.

The nurse came and put a screen around him. He died. In the morning, the bed was empty. We had all gone to sleep, despite the scurrying around the bed.

Mattie was a Negro woman attendant, fat and jolly. Not too fat, not too jolly. The day would hardly come up over the river, over there by Newtown Creek, before Mattie would be in to tidy up. First the dawn, then Mattie. They were alike — sure and certain. As she came in every morning, she would look over the ward with a glance to see that all her boys were still there.

"Aren't you ashamed of yourself?" she would ask. "Look the way you got your bed all rumped up. Push over, I'll fix it." And Mattie would fix the bed, straighten it out, make you feel somebody was taking care of you.

There was the time Olsen was gone. He was the pneumonia man — always getting pneumonia, and then, afterward, what the doctors call sequelae. That means what follows a disease. (A person picks up fragments of medicine while in Bellevue, usually incorrect fragments.) To take care of one of Olsen's sequelae, they were going to perform an operation. He had a good chance of getting out of the hospital for a little while before the operation if he played his cards right. There was a ball game in Brooklyn the night before his operation, and, sure enough, he was able to talk the doctors into giving him a pass to go out for the evening. "I'll be back by twelve o'clock, so tell the man at the gate let me in," he said to them. Before he left, Olsen came around to see me and told me that, according to the afternoon papers, Ralph Branca was going to pitch. The Brooks had a chance, a pretty good chance, he said. I noticed that he called them the Brooks and not the Bums or any other name by which they are referred to on the sports pages.

It was quite a thing for all of us, Olsen's going to the night game over in Brooklyn. First, he had to sign a paper to get his clothes back. They were rumply when he got them. In Bellevue, ordinarily, they take a patient's clothes away when he comes in and steam them, take the lice, if any, out of them, and put them away until the patient is going to leave. But, even so, Olsen looked pretty good in his clothes, better than in his bathrobe. I don't know where he got the money for the night game, but out he went. "So long, boys," he yelled down the ward as he gave his hat a tap. "I think Branca will pin their ears back. See you in the morning."

He wasn't there the next morning. He had overstayed his leave. He was AWOL. Mattie made Olsen's bed up — hopefully, it seemed. Two days passed, and Olsen was still not back. On the third morning, Mattie came in, glanced around, gave a tug to the cover of Olsen's bed, and walked through the ward to the big, arched window at my end. It was a foggy morning, and the air was nearly rain. The dampness in the streets almost got into the ward. Mattie looked out at the river and the fog. "Man, oh, man, this will wash him in," she said. "He can't take this, the lungs he got. This will wash him right back in here." Then she went and gave a couple of more tugs to Olsen's bed. Olsen never came back, at least not while I was there. We talked about him. Most of us figured he must have got to drinking after the game. Branca won it.

One day, in the middle of a bright afternoon, I looked up and Alfred the Armenian was standing by my bed. He said, "My name isn't Alfred. You got a schooling, I think. Well, my name is Mesrop. Alfred is easier, but my name is Mesrop. Do you know who Mesrop was?"

I told him I didn't know who Mesrop was.

"He was a hell of an Armenian," Alfred said. "Do you think that is much to be, a hell of an Armenian?"

"No," I said.

"Well, I think it is," said Alfred. "Do you know what Mesrop did?"

"Can't say as I do," I told him.

"He invented the alphabet, that's what he did," Alfred said.

"No kidding?" I said.

"Made up the whole alphabet," Alfred said. "He was a hell of an Armenian."

Alfred wandered away from my bed and went back to his own, across the ward and two down.

My wife came in to visit a few minutes afterward. She brought some cookies. While we were talking, I looked over and saw that Alfred was sitting in the straight-backed chair placed alongside his bed for the visitors who never came to see him. He had his hands folded on the bed, and his head was on his hands. "I think Alfred is crying," I said to my wife.

"Oh," she said. "I'll give him some cookies." She went over and nudged Alfred and gave him some cookies. I was right. He *was* crying.

He said thanks, ate a cookie, then strode over to me. Right in front of my wife, he said, "She thinks I'm a baby. She gave me some cookies to stop me crying."

"She's nuts," I said.

Alfred lit a cigarette and walked away.

The friends who came to visit a man when he is in a hospital like Bellevue become, for ever afterward, a special group in the man's mind. Even years later, whenever the man runs into one of them, he will identify him with a sudden, swift, unspoken thought: He came to see me at Bellevue. It isn't altogether easy or pleasant to go visiting in Bellevue. It's such a big, sprawling place that getting from the gate to a certain bedside is a task in itself. For us in the beds, our ward became the whole hospital as the weeks passed, for we hardly knew of the existence of the scores of other wards surrounding us, but to the visitor Bellevue was enormous, mystifying, and tortuous. Then, too, as the visitor makes his way through the place in crowded times like the pneumonia season, he is apt to come upon whole corridors lined with beds, upon which lie men who are gravely ill, and it sinks the visitor's heart. However contented we members of B-1 effortlessly were, our visitors always seemed a little depressed. After they had left, we often agreed that it was quite a job cheering them up.

Apparently, there is not a great deal for medical men to do about a heart case — or, to give it the name the cardiacs of the Vitamin Ward always used, "a bum ticker." The basic idea seems to be to keep the patient in bed and quiet. That is not to say that care was lacking in Ward B-1. Sometimes we used to think there was too much of it. It was not uncommon to be gone over by doctors seven or eight times in a day. That came about not wholly through solicitude for patients but largely because Bellevue is a teaching hospital as well as a healing hospital. The medical students of Columbia, Cornell, and N.Y.U. gain practical knowledge to supplement their classroom work by being taken through the wards by their teachers, who are older men, of medical eminence. Thus, the various wards are regarded as provinces of Cornell, N.Y.U., or Columbia. Ward B-1 was a Cornell ward.

At odd times of the day, we bed patients, always looking up and down the ward to watch the goings on of our world, would see a group of white-coated men gather around the nurses' desk, near the door. "Here comes the two-o'clock show," the Princeton 1911 man would say to me. Or perhaps it would be the four-o'clock show or the supper show. He knew, as we all knew, that the white-coated group was a professor of medicine (as well as a practicing notable, of course) and his students, and that they were about to come down the ward, stopping here and there and going over us.

To be sure, the medical lore a patient picks up in Bellevue is about comparable to the military law a soldier masters while he's a prisoner in the guardhouse — fragmentary, sometimes distorted, and often downright incorrect, yet to the soldier or the patient intensely interesting, since it concerns him pretty directly. Often enough, I was the subject of the teacher's brief talks and demonstrations ("the two-o'clock show"). A teacher that I remember was Dr. Cary Eggleston, who is one of the big cardiologists of the country. As he and the students stood around my bed, he would pick up one of my hands, for instance, turn it palm upward, and show it to his pupils. "Liver palm," he would say. That didn't sound any too complimentary, but I understood, as did the rest of us, that whatever was said in those sessions was really none of our business. We were eavesdropping, in a way.

There was some medicine administered during the routine of the day, of course, and what I heard about one particular drug caught my fancy. As a rule, neither nurses nor doctors, or anyone else, will let a patient know too much about the medicine he's getting, but sometimes they can be importuned into telling. A young technician, not a doctor, came in every day for a week or so and gave me capsules. Sometimes he gave me one, another time he would give me four, and a third time two. The range went all the way from one capsule to six. "Just what the hell are those capsules?" I asked him one day. He must have been feeling talky, because he told me. "It's an experimental thing," he said. "But don't let that alarm you. There's no danger."

"That's all right," I said.

"You know, don't you, that what caused your trouble was a clot?" he asked.

"Yes," I said.

"The stuff in the capsules is called dicumerol," he said. "It's not exactly new, but they don't know as much about it as they would like to. They hope it will serve to keep blood from clotting. You notice we take a blood test every day?"

"Certainly I notice," I said.

"That test daily is to show us what the previous day's capsule or capsules of dicumerol have done to your blood. You see, we are trying to find out what level is best in your particular case. We don't really know. We'll help you eventually, we hope, but the bigger idea is to use you as a means of adding just one small thing more to the store of knowledge about hearts."

"I get it," I said.

"Want to know how they came upon this drug?" he asked. He seemed to be a fellow of a nosy turn of mind, as, I would say, befits a fellow in a scientific field.

"How?" I asked.

"On certain farms, an unusual number of cows were losing their calves," he said. "That is, losing them before they were born. They looked into that and found that these cows were eating a certain kind of weed that thinned out their blood so much that it caused them to lose their calves. From that weed, they extracted the agent that was causing the trouble, and that's dicumerol. Properly controlled, it could possibly stop blood from clotting dangerously. And that's what we're trying to learn from you guys, if you don't mind."

"Don't mind a bit," I said.

In time, I stopped getting those capsules, for reasons best known to the doctors, so I didn't see the young technician for more than a week. Then, one day, I spied him across the ward, giving medicine to another bum-ticker man.

"Hey!" I hollered over to him.

"Oh, hello there," he said, and when he was through with the other man, he came over to my bed. "How're you doing?" he asked.

"All right, they say," I replied. "What did you learn from me about dicumerol?"

"Not a goddam thing," he said, and walked away.

*   *   *

We had one Bowery bum in Ward B-1. His name was Dooley, and he didn't weigh more than a hundred and two, give or take a pound. He was a panhandler on the outside. He made no bones about that. He was around sixty-three, and that is the way he had wound up, pan-handling. He had terrible arthritis in his legs, and the treatment he was getting required his legs to be in casts. He was in casts from the soles of his feet up to his thighs. Dooley was one of the fellows who didn't have any visitors. He shared other people's visitors. After your visitors had left, Dooley would ask, in a nice way, who they were. Conversation between Dooley and me had to be hollered, because we were so far apart in the ward.

"Hey, Mac!" Dooley hollered to me one morning. "Did I ever tell you how embarrassed I got once?"

"No," I hollered back.

"It was a time I twist my ankle," he said. "Come to think of it, I twist both of them, and I was drunk into the bargain. And on top of that it was the pneumonia season, and they were all jammed up in here. In the cor-ridors, everywhere. They take me in, but they have to throw me out in two days. Give me crutches, though. Brand-new crutches. I never had crutches before. Geez, it was icy outside. I had a hell of a time working the crutches. I start down the avenue toward the Bowery, and up comes an old man and give me something. I wasn't used to handling crutches and taking money at the same time. So I just hang on to what he give me with my right hand and say thanks and go along. 'I got dough,'

I say to myself, 'I guess I'll go to the movies.' Well, do you know what happens, Mac?"

"No," I said.

"I get up to that movie house — you know the one, on the west side of the street?"

"I know where you mean," I said.

"I walk up on the crutches to the window where the lady sells the tickets, and I unclutch my hand, and geez, what I have is a cent," Dooley said. "I been thinking all the time the old man give me a dime, and in those days you could get in the movies for a dime. My God, was I embarrassed! I didn't know what to do, so I say 'Excuse me' to the lady and go on down the avenue."

In Ward B-1, we did considerable grousing about the food, like soldiers in the army. The food at Bellevue is skimpy, but it will keep body and soul together, and the way one of the young doctors explained it to me, the primary idea at the hospital is to mend the body and patch it up, and that is more a question of medicine and instruments and apparatus than it is of food. He meant that Bellevue would rather economize on the food and spend more of its narrow budget on medicine and equipment, and when we patients chewed the matter over (in lieu of something better to chew), we tended to agree with him.

One thing there always seemed to be plenty of, though, was eggs. Breakfast for us bed patients usually consisted of a small bowl of porridge, fairly thin; two eggs, usually hard-boiled; a slice or two of bread; and some coffee, kind of weak. The eggs were in comparative abundance for a good reason. Prisoners on penal farms are kept busy raising hens, among other things, and the eggs that derive from the prisoners' forced industry go to public institutions like Bellevue. We all used to squirrel away a few eggs. Each patient, in the narrow space between his bed and the next fellow's, had a metal table with several shelves. For the time a man is in there, his worldly possessions are encompassed by the small space of those shelves: a towel, some soap, toilet articles, a book, maybe a letter or two — and, thanks to amiable thievery, a couple of eggs, against emergency hunger. The hospital doesn't hand out eggs to be hoarded; they are acquired by benign larceny, which is prevalent in Bellevue. At least, it was in Ward B-1.

When the food comes up to the ward, on rolling steam tables, from the kitchens, the walking patients have to help hand it out, because the nurses have too much else to do. Well, shortly after breakfast was over, Olsen (or some other walking patient) would come strolling along, an uncommon look of innocence on his face. He'd saunter up to the bedside, engage in the most immaculate of small talk. Then, out of the corner of his mouth, in the manner of a prisoner talking to a fellow convict in a jail yard, he'd say, "Could you use an egg, Mac?"

"Certainly could, pal," I'd say, also corner-of-the-mouth. And in a jiffy Olsen would dexterously slip a couple of hard-boiled eggs into the folds of my towel, on the shelf of my bedside table. A minute or two later, I'd see him doing the same thing for Dooley, across the way.

Olsen could hide more eggs more effectively than Fred Keating, the magician. It was a good feeling, I learned soon, to have a few eggs in reserve in Ward B-1.

Lucky lads, like myself, sometimes got help on the food problem from the outside. There was the matter of the steak. After a few weeks of Bellevue fare, a man actually dreams of steak, which is one item he doesn't get there. One day, when a friend of mine came to visit, I mentioned the steak mirages we all had. My friend keeps a tavern in the Forties, where I had assailed many a sirloin. "Don't eat any supper tomorrow," he said. "I'm coming in."

About six o'clock the next afternoon, I looked down the ward, as I had been doing every minute or two since five o'clock, and I saw my friend heading toward me in a great rush. He was burdened heavily with something ponderously wrapped in towels and napkins. He practically ran up to the bedside, and sweat was glistening on his face and his eyes were popping. He put his burden on the bed, hastily unwrapped it, and there was a steaming steak as big as a banjo, with onions and French fries beautifully girdling it. "Wade into this!" he said, and he whisked a sharp knife and a fork out of his pocket, where he had had them, wrapped in a napkin. The smell of steak got into the air, and right away practically everybody in the ward was staring at my bed. "Man alive!" I said. "This is too much for me."

It really was, so I hailed Princeton 1911 and Olsen to join me in the steak, and got the nurse to cut off a couple chunks and take them over to the encased Dooley. It was marvelous eating, we all agreed. "How in the world did you get that steak here piping hot and everything?" I asked my friend as I settled back luxuriously on the pillow.

He laughed. "Well, I guess I might get in bad if anyone found out," he said. "And maybe a cop would get the sack. But you got to maneuver things in this town; you got to get guys to rally around when somebody's in a jam."

"Explain yourself," I said to him. "I don't know what you're talking about."

He grinned at the sight of Princeton 1911, Olsen, Dooley, and myself so well fed, and said, "There's a motorcycle cop comes into the store [the saloon is always "the store" with my friend] for a little slug now and then. Especially on cold days, when it is bitter on one of those motorcycles. He has one slug and let's it go at that. Good cop, not a scrounger. Well, when you told me a steak would come in handy, I wondered at first how the hell I could get it all those twenty blocks and more and still have it hot for you. Then it came to me. I explained the situation to the motorcycle cop, and he said, 'This is official business on behalf of a bona fide taxpayer of the City of New York.' That's what he said. He told me have the steak ready at quarter of six on the dot. And at twenty to six he came in and asked where's the steak? It was ready, and the cop said for me to wrap it up well and come on. He had a taxi waiting right outside the door, and what does he do, after I get into the cab with the steak, but jump on his motorcycle and speed off ahead of the cab. In two seconds, we were roaring down the street, with the siren howling. We went through lights fifty miles an hour, like nobody's business, and I bet it didn't take us four minutes to get down here. Regular motorcycle escort. The cop beat it as soon as the cab got to the gate. He stopped a minute and told me not to say anything about what he did. The Commissioner might not approve, he said, but what the hell! How was the steak, anyway?"

"It was goddam good," I said.

"I'll say it was goddam good," said Princeton 1911.

"Me, too," Dooley hollered over.

"You can say that again," said Olsen.

One bird of passage blew into Ward B-1. He came in during the night, while we were all asleep, and he was put in Olsen's bed, because this was the time when Olsen was AWOL. "Bird" is not the right word for him. The poor man looked just like a marmoset, his face was so small and he was so frail. He had the same kind of darting, shoe-button eyes as a marmoset, and he also had the same evident desire to ingratiate himself.

When we looked at this newcomer next morning, the first thing we saw was a pip of a shiner. His right eye was in a setting of black and purple and magenta, which made the eye itself look all the more bright. His right forearm was in a splint. Ordinarily, injured men didn't get into B-1, but this fellow was only an overnight guest, so to speak, and Olsen's bed happened to be empty.

Alfred the Armenian halted at his bed and asked him

what was the matter. "Something must have happened to me," the little man said. "I got a kind of a black eye and what they call a fractured noola." One half of this announcement — the black-eye part — was an enormously unnecessary statement, and the other half was mystifying. It was some time before we figured it out. The marmoset man had evidently peeked at the description of his injuries that the doctors had written down on his record, and he had got a little balled up in his anatomical terms. He had a fracture of the ulna, and the word must have looked to him, through his black eye, like "nula," which he pronounced "noola." They sent him out after lunch, and we all promptly forgot about him, except to ask, once in a while during an idle moment, "I wonder whatever became of the noola man?"

The evening and early morning were the best times in Ward B-1. The food in Bellevue is scanty, as I said, so the snack that came around on a rolling table at eight-fifteen at night was a big event. Before Olsen went to the night game and never came back, he was the one who pushed the table around. The nurses do not have time for such chores, and so walking patients, like Olsen, take over. About eight o'clock, nearly three hours after dinner, we would begin thinking, and often talking, about the snack.

"I hope they have cocoa tonight," Dooley would say.

"I think they *will* have cocoa," Milton, the Brooklyn cabdriver, might reply. "They had grapefruit juice now two nights hand-running. I think it will be cocoa."

The snack that Olsen wheeled around usually consisted of a couple of slices of bread and something to drink — sometimes it was grapefruit juice, occasionally plain milk, if some was left over from dinner, and, on big nights, cocoa. I would watch Olsen make his way along the ward to my bed, and all the while my appetite would grow. Finally, the table would be in front of my bed, and Olsen would say, "Cocoa, Mac, or what?"

"Cocoa," I would say.

"How about you, Mr. Darton?" Olsen would ask the Princeton 1911 man, in the bed on my right.

"Don't mind if I do," the Princeton man would say. And in a minute we would all be having our slice of bread and our cocoa, and talking bed to bed. "What a bunch of chumps up there at the Racquet Club," the Princeton man said to me one night. "They think they're living high. Chumps. That's what they are, eh, Mac?"

"What could be better than this?" I said.

"Isn't that river pretty?" he asked, waving a chunk of bread at the arched window. "Look at all those lights." A tug was coming down in the dark, and strung above her were red and green lights, betokening to oncoming vessels what kind of tow she had behind her.

"Real handsome little river," I said. The cocoa was good, and we were all happy for a while.

Heart cases usually stay in the hospital for from six to eight weeks. When my day to go home came around, I found I was to go out as I had come in — on a stretcher. But the stretcher was now a precaution, rather than a necessity. The nurse brought my clothes, to be taken, but not worn, home. Right away, I noticed that they were unwrinkled and did not have that shrunken look that Olsen's had had. "How come my clothes aren't all rumpled up like Olsen's?" I asked her.

"I guess the attendant noticed that you were brought in from a good hotel, and figured he wouldn't bother to delouse them," she said.

"Caste system?" I asked. "Is that creeping in here?"

"No," the nurse said. "The man was merely saving wear and tear on the delousing machine, that's all."

My wife took charge of getting my clothes home, and I got onto the stretcher myself. On the way out, naturally, I was wheeled along between the rows of beds. We B-1 veterans had been talking for a couple of days about my going home. As well as we had known each other, we hadn't said anything about looking each other up sometime on the outside. All of us were grown-up enough to know that such promises are never kept. Dooley hollered good-by and good luck from his bed, and so did the others, as the stretcher went by. Bellevue fellows are always glad when somebody — anybody — has won out over whatever was the matter with him, and, thanks to what had been done for me (I had done nothing for myself except be obedient), I had won out. While they were hollering good-by, I knew they were thinking about the day they'd go home, too. Even Dooley, who could look forward only to going back to the Bowery, had told me that he had a couple of pals down there he'd like to say hello to once again.

4

〰〰〰〰〰〰〰〰〰〰〰〰〰〰〰〰〰〰〰〰〰〰〰〰〰〰〰〰〰〰〰〰〰

The Jackpot

〰〰〰〰〰〰〰〰〰〰〰〰〰〰〰〰〰〰〰〰〰〰〰〰〰〰〰〰〰〰〰〰〰

THE DIARY of Mrs. Jane Caffrey, the slim, good-looking
wife of James P. Caffrey, of Wakefield, Rhode Island,
says, for Saturday, August 28, 1948: "Took kids to beach
in the morning. Very hot. Jim and I went to clambake in
afternoon at Willow Dell. Asked a few people to house
for late afternoon. Jim won $24,000 jackpot on 'Sing It
Again' program. Everybody excited." This would be an
extraordinary entry in anybody's diary, and it is especially notable for the seeming calmness with which Mrs.
Caffrey recorded the great good fortune of her husband.
I would not know of this entry in the diary, or of other
things about that historic day in the life of the Caffreys,
had I not been a friend of Jim Caffrey's long before the
twenty-eighth of August. After he won the jackpot —

realizing the ambition of millions of people in the United States — I resolved to reconstruct exactly what took place that evening and then keep close track of everything that happened to Caffrey as a result of his success. This I have tried to do.

The Caffreys are substantial people in Wakefield. Mrs. Caffrey is the daughter of Grafton Kenyon, whose grandfather, William G. Kenyon, founded Kenyon's Department Store in 1856. It is the only department store in Wakefield. Caffrey works in the family store. He is thirty-five and fair-haired, and looks like a photogenic football player. When he was at Providence College, from which he graduated in 1936, he did play some football. The Caffreys, who have two children — a seven-year-old daughter named Carol and a four-year-old son named Kenyon — live in a pleasant twelve-room house of two and a half stories. It is painted white and has a well-kept lawn on three sides.

When the Caffreys drove home from the clambake at the Willow Dell Beach Club, a little before six o'clock that Saturday afternoon, they left their 1946 Pontiac sedan in the driveway back of the house and went inside to prepare for the guests they had invited. In a few minutes the phone rang. Caffrey answered, and a girl who said she was with the Columbia Broadcasting System in New York asked if he was James P. Caffrey, of 20 Kenyon Avenue, Wakefield, Rhode Island. He said he was, and she asked, "Will you be home tonight between eight and nine o'clock to listen to 'Sing It Again,' on C.B.S.?"

"I *can* be home," Caffrey said. He suspected a joke, because the fellows who hang around Al Weibel's newspaper store and Gene Wilcox's garage are great ones for playing jokes involving phone calls. "What's it all about? What's it all about?" Caffrey asked the girl, politely but in the tone that is employed for letting pranksters know that one is not being taken in.

"Well, Mr. Caffrey, your telephone number has been picked as one of those to call during the program tonight," the girl explained. "You may have a chance at the twenty-four-thousand-dollar jackpot. You'll be home, won't you? We have to be sure, so the program can go right along without any 'Don't answer's or 'Busy's. Be sure not to use your phone between eight o'clock and nine o'clock, so the line will be open for us when we call."

"Oh, all right, I'll be home," Caffrey said. He still felt fairly certain it was a gag.

Mrs. Caffrey was upstairs, getting Carol ready for bed. Caffrey went up to tell her about the phone call. He was careful to begin by saying, "You know, this may all be kidding by somebody over at Al's or Gene's place . . ." He pointed out, however, that the phone call unquestionably came from New York. When Carol heard the news, she, naturally, protested, quite energetically, against going to bed at her seven-o'clock bedtime.

"Oh, no, Carol," her mother said, "You heard what Daddy said. It's just a joke, that's all." Still protesting, Carol went to bed. Mrs. Caffrey got Kenyon into his bed, in the room across the hall, and she and her husband went downstairs.

"I've never heard 'Sing It Again.' Have you?" Caffrey said. Mrs. Caffrey didn't remember hearing the program. Their guests, who had also been to the clambake, started to arrive, happily sated with lobsters, clams, sweet corn, and watermelon. The Caffreys got busy with the cocktail shaker. They held back the news for a few minutes, but then they decided to take a chance and tell about it.

"Jim, you'll never have to work another day if you win it," one of the guests said. "Twenty-four thousand smackers!"

"Are you sure you people didn't frame up that call at the bake?" Caffrey asked. "Oh, well! What have I got to lose? I'm going to listen at eight o'clock anyhow."

"We're all going to listen," another guest said. "This is the biggest night in Wakefield since the hurricane. The jackpot! Twenty-four thousand bucks!"

By five minutes after seven, the predicament of the Caffreys was painful. The kidding was all well and good, but, as one of the guests had remarked, without contradiction, twenty-four thousand dollars is twenty-four thousand dollars. It was impossible to think about getting supper, but nobody eats much after the abundance of a Rhode Island clambake anyway. The guests were still arriving. The early arrivals were now phoning friends and asking them over to the Caffreys', and the living room was becoming crowded. "They're going to call Jim from New York and let him have a whack at the jackpot on some program. It's twenty-four thousand dollars! Can you imagine that? Hurry up over! The whole gang's here!"

Curiously, considering the popularity of the "Sing It Again" program, none of the guests could give the Caffreys much of a notion of what it was like.

"I think they ask you to tell the name of a certain tune they play," one of them said.

"No, that's 'Stop the Music,'" another one said.

"Isn't this the program that has the Phantom Voice or something like that?" another guest asked. "I think it is. In fact, I'm sure it is."

"Gosh, I don't know," said Mrs. Caffrey. "Neither does Jim. Now, isn't that just our luck? All the radio programs we listen to, and we never heard this one. Oh, maybe somebody's kidding us, as Jim says. It doesn't matter. We'll all have some fun. What time is it, anyhow? The program's at eight o'clock."

It was ten minutes after seven. What with all the guests, it was a while before Jim and Jane Caffrey could get off to talk to each other privately. Then one Caffrey (neither of them remembers which one it was) managed to say to the other, "Wouldn't it be great, with our anniversary Tuesday and twenty-four thousand dollars?" They decided that it would be a shrewd idea to phone some people and ask if they had any dope on "Sing It Again." After trying a couple of other friends without learning anything, Caffrey called me, at a cabin in a woods ten miles from his house. I was sitting in on a Saturday-night poker game. I couldn't help him, either, because, as I told him, I try not to listen to give-away programs.

"Is there anybody you can call in New York who might know?" Caffrey asked.

"I'll do what I can," I told him.

I thought of a friend of mine, David Broekman, a composer and conductor of symphonies who sometimes conducts on the radio. I got him on long distance and he said, "Well, they have a riddle, a kind of jingle lyric set to a popular tune, and that is usually easy to guess. When you guess that, why, they let you guess at the Phantom Voice. That's on a recording, and they've been guessing it wrong for eight or ten weeks now, I believe."

"Have you any idea whose voice it is?" I asked.

"Well, the best dope I hear around is that it is either Irving Berlin or Louis B. Mayer. But, to tell the truth, I don't know. I don't listen particularly — just offhand. But you know yourself Irving Berlin's voice is high-pitched, sort of, and he has a New York accent. Mayer's is lower and he almost sounds British. He's from Haverhill, Massachusetts, you know, so there's a little New England accent there. But listen. I'm not sure it's either one of those two. Gee whizz! Don't blame me if it's wrong."

"No, no, thanks, good-by," I said hurriedly, and perhaps brusquely, because I wanted to give Caffrey this news as soon as I could. Luckily, his line was not busy, and I told him what Broekman had said. I was scared of losing a friend if I was wrong, so I tacked on, "Don't blame me, Jimmy, if it isn't either Berlin or Mayer, but that's the best information I can get."

"No, no, thanks, good-by," Caffrey said, eerily repeating the very words I had just spoken to Broekman.

At five minutes to eight, when the house was full of guests, all talking at once, the Caffreys made an alarming discovery — the radio and the telephone were pretty far apart. The radio was in the living room and the telephone was out in the hall. It would be difficult, perhaps impossible, in that crowd, to listen for the phone and at the same time pay close attention to the radio. Caffrey ran upstairs, two steps at a clip, and brought down a small radio from his and Mrs. Caffrey's bedroom and plugged it in not far from the telephone. He then sat beside the phone, and Mrs. Caffrey stood in front of the living-room radio. She was too nervous to sit. As eight o'clock approached, the guests began to quiet down.

"Sing It Again" came on the air. Broekman had described it accurately. The master of ceremonies, Dan Seymour, said, after the opening hullabaloo, "Now listen to this voice!" Then the low-pitched Phantom Voice was heard, singing, to the tune of "Pop Goes the Weasel!":

> Twinkle, twinkle, up in the blue,
> And I'm not in the middle.
> Take a ten, divide it by two.
> Pop goes the riddle!

There was dismay on every face in the Caffrey living room. The riddle sounded like complete gibberish. The guests looked at one another blankly, for this abracadabra did not seem to fit either Mayer or Berlin. Then everyone wanted to talk and the radio was nearly drowned out. "Sh-h-h! Sh-h-h!" Mrs. Caffrey said. "Listen to those prizes!"

In the manner of radio, the announcer shouted, "THE TWENTY–FOUR–THOUSAND–DOLLAR JACK–POT!," speaking in capital letters. Two other voices then alternated in the recital of the dazzling list of prizes, each voice, in its turn, mounting in volume and intensity.

"A Cavalier hope chest!" said one voice excitedly.

"A thousand-dollar Bulova wrist watch!" barked the other voice.

"A two-thousand-dollar Columbia diamond ring!"

"An Ansley television receiver!"

"A Vita-Var paint-and-varnish supply for your entire house! Inside and out!"

"And Jencraft Venetian blinds for your entire home!"

"A Westinghouse refrigerator!"

"A Westinghouse range!"

"A Westinghouse Laundromat!"

"A Lennox heating system for your home!"

"A Virginia House dining-room suite and bedroom suite!"

"A Cavalier cedar chest — stocked with five dozen Spring Maid sheets and pillowcases!"

"A Kelvinator Home Freezer — plus a three-year supply of Snow Crop frozen foods for a family of four!"

"A complete steer, dressed and delivered to your home!"

"A General Electric automatic dishwasher!"

"Two thousand dollars' worth of Stark fruit trees!"

"An airplane trip for two persons for two weeks to Elko, Nevada, arranged by V.I.P. Service, New York!"

"A complete set of Amelia Earhart luggage, all in Parisian pink!"

"A Ceil Chapman vacation wardrobe!"

"A men's wardrobe of Eagle Clothes!"

"Your portrait painted in oil, by Fred Wright, of New York City!"

"A Darra-James workshop, complete with motors!"

"Seven thousand five hundred cans of Phillips Delicious Foods!"

"A two-thousand-dollar Trane air-conditioner for your home!"

"A new 1949 Ford custom-built sedan!"

As each item on the list was announced, the Caffreys and their guests laughed almost hysterically.

Finally, the m.c. said that telephone calls would be made to people all over the country. To each person who answered, a special lyric, containing a riddle, would be sung, to a familiar tune. If the contestant solved this riddle, the Phantom Voice record would be played again and the contestant would be asked whose voice it was.

Then an orchestra began to play, and intervals of music were broken by the sound of a buzzer, which meant that a phone call had been put through to one of the listeners, who had presumably been alerted, like the Caffreys. The announcer's end of the conversations could be heard over the radio. There were calls to Centralia, Illinois;

Springfield, Massachusetts; Nanticoke, Pennsylvania; Jersey City, New Jersey; San Antonio, Texas; Marion, Indiana; Cleveland, Ohio; Omaha, Nebraska; Geneva, New York; and Gainesville, Georgia. Six people were able to solve the preliminary riddle but were unable to name the owner of the Phantom Voice. Caffrey, sitting at his phone, stared at it, in the hope of hypnotizing it into ringing. Fifty minutes of the hour passed and it still hadn't rung.

Upstairs, Carol was wide-awake. Every once in a while, she shouted down to her mother. First, she wanted a drink of water. When she was told to get it in the bathroom, she said, "No, I mean orange juice." "Please, please, Carol!" her mother shouted. "We'll tell you all about this later!" Carol's brother Kenyon slept through everything. The Caffreys' two dogs — Gretchen, a dachshund, and Whiskey, an aged Scotty — were in a dither. Usually, Whiskey spent his evenings drowsing on the floor. This night, he went about ceaselessly on his slow legs, smelling drinks on the coffee table (that's how he got his name), smelling shoes, and getting in everyone's nervous way.

At seven minutes to nine, the Caffrey phone rang. Everybody fell silent. Caffrey hastily picked up the phone, put his face almost into the mouthpiece, and tremulously said, "Hello?" Guests clustered around him, bending over to listen. "Jim," they heard someone say, "we were wondering if you and Jane would like to come over — "

"Hang up! Hang up!" Caffrey shouted. "Can't talk!

Can't talk!" He slammed the phone back onto the cradle. "That was Eddie Martin," he said. "Must be the only guy in South County doesn't know what's going on."

At five minutes to nine, the Caffreys had all but given up. Seymour was talking to someone in Bakersfield, California. That contestant failed, too. The Caffrey phone rang again. This time, it was C.B.S. The switchboard girl asked Caffrey to hold the line, and said she would speak to him every few seconds, to make sure he was still on. Thirty seconds passed.

"Is this Mr. James Caffrey, of 20 Kenyon Avenue, Wakefield, Rhode Island?" Seymour asked over the air.

Caffrey could hear the same thing three ways, the announcer talking to him on the phone and the words coming out of the two radios. "Yes, this is Jim Caffrey," he replied shakily.

"The Riddlers' Quartet has just sung 'Do Ye Ken John Peel?,' Mr. Caffrey," Seymour said. "Now, Mr. Caffrey, do ye ken these two comic characters they are going to sing about now? Listen, Mr. Caffrey!"

A harmony team sang, to the tune of "John Peel":

> Do ye ken Ken Kling,
> With his horses to play?
> Do ye ken Ken Kling,
> With his big parlay?
> Or if Joe woulda stood in bed that day,
> Then you wouldn't find me in mourning!

Caffrey, trying to think of too many things at once, had no idea what the answer was. But from the living room Jane yelled, "Joe and Asbestos, Jim! Joe and Asbestos!"

"Joe and Asbestos," Caffrey said into the receiver.

"Absolutely correct, Mr. Caffrey!" the announcer shouted. (Joe and Asbestos are two race-track characters created by Ken Kling, who gives tips on horse races in a syndicated comic strip.)

"Mr. Caffrey, you have won a beautiful Cavalier hope chest!" Seymour shouted ecstatically. "Now you have a chance to parlay that hope chest into twenty-four thousand dollars' worth of prizes! Are you ready? Listen to the Phantom Voice!"

Once again, for the eighth time that night, the Caffreys heard "Twinkle, twinkle, up in the blue . . ."

"Can you pop that twenty-four-thousand-dollar riddle, Mr. Caffrey?" Seymour asked.

"I think it is Louis B. Mayer, of Hollywood, California," Caffrey said, with amazingly meticulous diction.

"Will you please repeat that?" Seymour demanded.

"I think it is Louis B. Mayer, of Hollywood, California," Caffrey said again.

"Louis B. Mayer?" Seymour repeated, for millions to hear. "That is absolutely right, Mr. Caffrey, up there in Wakefield, Rhode Island! YOU HAVE WON THE TWENTY-FOUR-THOUSAND-DOLLAR JACKPOT!"

In the happy ruckus that broke loose in the Caffreys' house, someone, historical-minded, looked at his watch. It was 8:57, three minutes before the end of the program.

"Mr. Caffrey, how long have you known the Phantom Voice was Louis B. Mayer?" Seymour asked.

"Oh, a couple of weeks," said Caffrey, and turned and winked at his guests.

"A couple of weeks! And you hung on and we called you!" Seymour said. Then he, too, was apparently overcome by the tenseness of the moment, for he went on confusedly, "Mr. Wakefield, up there in Rhode Island, you were ABSOLUTELY RIGHT!"

Somehow, the Caffreys and their guests managed to listen as Seymour continued, "You were right! 'Twinkle, twinkle, up in the blue' — that meant the stars in Metro-Goldwyn-Mayer's studio! And 'I'm not in the middle' — that meant Louis Mayer was not in the middle. Goldwyn is in the middle and Mayer on the end. Metro-Goldwyn-*Mayer*. And 'Take a ten, divide it by two' — that means five, and there are five letters in 'L-o-u-i-s,' and five letters in 'M-a-y-e-r.'" All this was very interesting information — and news — in the home of the Caffreys, where the twenty-four-thousand-dollar jackpot had just been won.

"And by way of an extra hint, the fifth sign of the zodiac is Leo!" Seymour said. "And Leo is the lion who roars in all the Metro-Goldwyn-Mayer movies!" At 20 Kenyon Avenue, Wakefield, Rhode Island, that precious bit of knowledge was hilarious news indeed.

"Those twenty-four thousand dollars' worth of prizes are on their way!" Seymour concluded. "Clear the tracks to Wakefield, Rhode Island!"

It was nine o'clock. The program ended. The guests

at the Caffreys' were screaming with delight, kissing each other, all trying to throw their arms around Caffrey and Mrs. Caffrey. Carol, in her nightdress, ran down the stairs into the turmoil and into the arms of her mother. (Weeks later, Mrs. Caffrey said, "All I can remember is that Carol looked just like an ad for kids' nighties when she ran downstairs!") Caffrey was by now in the middle of the living room, being whirled around by guests.

"Daddy won twenty-four thousand dollars, Carol!" Mrs. Caffrey cried.

"I heard it all! I heard it all! I was hiding behind the banister!" Carol yelled. Her mother told her to go upstairs and put on her bathrobe, then come back down and have some ginger ale.

The phone rang again. It was the Providence *Journal*, wanting to interview Caffrey about the jackpot. What was he going to do with all the things he had won? Caffrey said he didn't know. How about the seventy-five hundred cans of soup, the *Journal* asked. Later on, Caffrey realized that of the twenty-eight prizes in the jackpot, what caught the fancy of most people was the "seventy-five hundred cans of soup." The prize was actually seventy-five hundred cans of food of many kinds, but people had got the idea that it was all soup, and they seemed fascinated and vastly amused by the idea of a family's suddenly coming into possession of seventy-five hundred cans of soup.

As soon as the Providence *Journal* had hung up, the phone rang again. It was a call from a woman in New

York, a stranger, whose name Caffrey did not catch. "I'm so glad you won it, especially because I helped you," the woman said. "I listen all the time, and when I like people, I pray for them. I prayed for you." Caffrey thanked her and hung up.

Another call came, from a police matron at Providence Police Headquarters. "I remember you when you were a policeman here," she said. "You used to have nice curly yellow hair, didn't you?" "Maybe I did," said the fussed Caffrey. "Thank you, thank you." He had once been a motorcycle cop in Providence, to help pay his way through college after his father's death.

The phone kept ringing. Caffrey finally managed to break away from the house, by saying that he had to go to the Wakefield Diner and get some more ice from Berry Whiting. The walk gave him a chance to calm himself and to try to realize what had happened to him. He couldn't, quite.

The last of the guests didn't leave until after four, and even then the phone was still ringing every once in a while.

At seven o'clock in the morning on Sunday, August 29th, the day after Caffrey won the jackpot, he drove up to my house in Wakefield, where I was spending the summer. His face was sorrowful and puzzled. We often have coffee together early on summer mornings, and I had expected that if he came to my place that morning, he would practically dance out of his car.

"This is silly, having things happen this way," he said.

"What's the matter with you?" I asked. "You're the luckiest man in the land."

"I've just been burying the dog," he said.

He and his wife had not been able to go to sleep. They had talked about the two-thousand-dollar diamond ring they had won, the two thousand dollars' worth of fruit trees, the television set, the airplane trip to Elko, the custom-built Ford sedan, the thousand-dollar wrist watch, the electric refrigerator, the air-conditioning unit, the Venetian blinds, the complete set of luggage, and the prize they regarded as absurd — having Caffrey's portrait painted in oil. "I got up at six o'clock," Caffrey said, over our coffee. "I thought I'd take a ride down by the beach and try to think this thing out. When I looked out the front window, Whiskey was lying there on the lawn. I knew the minute I saw him he was dead." Whiskey had, of course, been very lively, for him, the night before. "At his age, he was bound to die any day," Caffrey went on. "He was past sixteen years old. Just the same, it does seem ridiculous to have it happen on this morning, of all mornings. I mean on top of the jackpot and all that excitement last night. Maybe the excitement, and having so many people around, was what really killed Whiskey. I had to take him out in the woods and bury him right away. I was afraid the kids might wake up and see him dead. I wouldn't want them to do that."

"He *was* pretty old," I said.

"Yes, that's what I said," Caffrey answered. "But I hate to see him go, just the same. Funny that it should be this morning, isn't it?"

One of the first things Caffrey wanted to talk about that morning was how he could show his gratitude to David Broekman for helping him win the jackpot. So, with Caffrey standing by, I telephoned Broekman, thanked him in Caffrey's behalf, and said that Caffrey wanted him to have some share in the winnings, when they materialized.

"Forget about it," said Broekman. "I'm glad the boy won, and please tell him to let it go at that."

"Well, how about a case of Scotch?" I asked Broekman, at Caffrey's suggestion.

"Don't drink, myself," said Broekman, "but if he feels that way about it, why, a case of Scotch does come in handy around the house."

"Tell him I'll send him three cases," Caffrey prompted.

I told Broekman that, and he laughed and asked me to congratulate the winner for him.

After having our coffee, Caffrey and I went downtown to Al Weibel's store for the Sunday papers. Weibel's is a favorite gathering place in Wakefield, and the minute Caffrey entered, he was surrounded by people. They slapped him on the back and said, over and over again, "A twenty-four-thousand-dollar jackpot! Twenty-four thousand dollars! Some dough for Jimmy Caffrey! Twenty-four-thousand bucks!" Everybody in the store knew that figure. Everybody seemed to like to say it. Caffrey was obviously trying to be modest about his good fortune, but he was understandably proud of it. "I certainly was lucky," he said repeatedly. All of them had read the story in the Providence *Journal*. The head-

line was "24,000 IN RADIO PRIZES TAKEN BY FORMER
PROVIDENCE POLICEMAN," and the story said, in part:

The winner, James Caffrey of Kenyon Avenue,
Wakefield, a former Providence patrolman and now
a floor manager at Kenyon's Department Store, Wakefield, was worried by just one thing — where is he
going to store 7500 cans of soup, one of the major
items in the all-inclusive prize.

Caffrey won the embarrassment of riches that
threatens to engulf his house by correctly identifying
Louis B. Mayer as the owner of the "phantom voice"
after listening to an abstruse riddle on the "Sing It
Again" show.

Of particular note any day in view of present high
food prices is a "complete" steer, suitably reduced to
steaks and roasts, and a three-year supply of frozen
foods — with a home-freezer for the storage thereof.

The fellows in Weibel's agreed that the jackpot was
certainly one of the biggest things that had ever happened to Wakefield. And when Caffrey read the story,
he said, "I forgot all about the steer, and so did Jane. We
can't remember all the things on the list, and I forgot
all about the steer, for one thing. Wonder what we'll
do with *that*."

After Caffrey got the Sunday papers, he went home,
and I went along with him. "Daddy, I looked everywhere and nothing's come!" Carol said as we arrived.
"I looked all over the house and out on the porch and
on the lawn, and nothing's come at all! Not a single
thing!"

When Seymour had yelled, "Those twenty-four thousand dollars' worth of prizes are on their way! Clear the tracks to Wakefield, Rhode Island!" Carol had taken him literally, and she was grossly disappointed at not finding the house filled with fruit trees, diamond rings, and other treasures when she came downstairs that morning. Caffrey assured her that the prizes would come, all right. Kenyon, who stood around in the living room looking happily from one to another of us, didn't understand exactly what had happened the night before, but he realized that it was something wonderful and he was enjoying the excitement.

Mrs. Caffrey came in from the kitchen. "The phone began ringing soon after you left, Jim," she said. "I guess we'll hear from everyone in South County about that twenty-four thousand dollars. Don't you think we'd better take the children to the beach and get away from the phone calls?"

That afternoon, the Caffrey family and I went to the beach club. It was the same there as it had been in Weibel's. Mr. and Mrs. Caffrey were the center of interest, and they had to tell the story of the previous night dozens of times. Finally, Caffrey sent Carol to the club office for their bathhouse keys. Half an hour later, when she hadn't returned, he and I went looking for her. We found her surrounded by a crowd of kids and adults, who were asking her about the family's stroke of luck. Carol was giving her version of what had happened, and her playmates were marveling at the coming of such a high-powered Christmas in late August.

During that day of glory, I noticed that Caffrey, under the stress of frequent congratulations, was forced to adopt a formalized reply to well-wishers, something like the remarks that movie stars have for people who crowd around them. "Thank you, thank you," he would say. "Oh, it won't be quite twenty-four thousand, I'm afraid. That's a radio figure, you know. And don't forget, those tax boys will be after me. Still, I was pretty lucky, I guess."

I spoke to Caffrey about his sounding like a movie actor, and he admitted that he had noticed it himself. "When I was a cop in Providence, they used to assign me to escort visiting movie stars," he said. "And I saw then that they all had little set speeches for when people were around them. Can you imagine me doing the same thing? This is one hell of a country, isn't it, when you can suddenly get a phone call and there's some kind of monkey business on the radio and the next day you're famous or something, and tons of prizes are on the way to your house! Seems a little silly to me."

Now and then, during the rest of the day, Caffrey discussed the prize list with me — which things he and Jane planned to sell, which things they planned to keep. "Of course, it isn't going to be any twenty-four thousand dollars," he said. "I've got sense enough to know that. Practically everybody I talk to turns out to be some sort of tax expert, but so far I haven't been able to get any official dope." Then he decided that if "the stuff," as he had begun to call the prizes, turned out to be worth eighteen thousand dollars, he would have to pay about a

50 per cent tax on it, and that would leave him nine thousand dollars. "Even that isn't bad, is it?" he said.

By Sunday night, the Caffreys were weary of talking to everybody they met about their good luck. Since Kenyon's Department Store is closed on Mondays as well as Sundays, and Caffrey didn't have to work, they decided to go to Block Island for the day, on a cabin cruiser owned by a friend. (The island lies in the Atlantic, twelve miles off Point Judith, a famed promontory not far from Wakefield.)

"When we tied up at the dock on Block Island," Caffrey told me upon their return, "the first guy who came up to me asked about the twenty-four-thousand-dollar jackpot! I guess one of the fellows on the boat must have told this islander about it the minute we touched the pier. And this islander said the very same words, exactly, that I bet a dozen people have said to me in the last couple of days. He said, 'By God, I'm glad to meet somebody at last that won one of those things! It's usually somebody way out West that wins them.' "

Caffrey did not say so, but I noticed that by Tuesday evening the endless repetition of the words "twenty-four-thousand-dollar jackpot" had begun to get on his nerves. He was too mannerly to tell anybody that, yet he winced when he heard the phrase. That was the figure people had in their heads, and if Caffrey was determined not to build castles in the air, his friends seemed equally determined to set him up as a man who suddenly had twenty-four thousand dollars in cold, new cash in his pocket.

The Caffreys celebrated their eighth wedding anniversary, the Tuesday after "the day of the jackpot" (around the Caffrey house, events were being dated that way), by giving another party. It was inevitable that some of the guests should bring boxes of crackers. "You'll need them for all that soup," they said.

"Those seventy-five hundred cans of soup are one thing we're going to get rid of," Caffrey said, by this time stringing along with the people who insisted on lumping all the assorted canned goods together as soup. The Caffreys told the guests their plans for some of the other prizes, too. They would keep the deep freeze, because they did not have one, and the television set, a thing they had never even thought of buying. They could use the electric range, as the one they had was prewar, and they would keep the washing machine. "We think the trip to Nevada ought to be nice," Mrs. Caffrey said. "We've never been out that way, and after the first of the year Jim can probably get away from the store for a couple of weeks and I can make some arrangement about Carol and Kenyon, and Nevada ought to be fun." Caffrey's favorite prize was the car. The Caffreys' 1946 Pontiac sedan was in good shape, but they had been trying for two years to replace it with a station wagon. They figured that they would use the Ford custom sedan as a trade-in for a station wagon and pay the difference out of the proceeds of the sale of the Pontiac.

*   *   *

The luck of the Caffreys was far too big a thing to be overlooked by the alert and enterprising Narragansett *Times,* the weekly newspaper that serves South County. In its issue of September 3rd, the Friday after the day of the jackpot, the *Times* said in an editorial:

> What pleased us most about the success of our Mr. Caffrey in winning the $24,000 radio jackpot last Saturday evening was the fact that Mrs. Caffrey had a vital part. Had it not been for her help in giving Jim the answer to the first riddle, he would never have had the chance to name the mystery voice.
>
> The achievement of our Wakefield couple, then, gives us a dramatic example of the value of teamwork — an example which any married couple knows is sound and necessary if domestic felicity is to be the rudder in guiding the matrimonial barque.
>
> We salute the Caffreys, not only in solving the riddle of the mystery voice, but for bringing to Wakefield national publicity by their accomplishments.

This editorial pleased Caffrey, because most people were giving him all the credit for making the right answers and he wanted Mrs. Caffrey to receive her share.

The first of the prizes to arrive was the two-thousand-dollar diamond ring. This came on Tuesday, September 7th. It was the earliest material evidence that the whole episode was not a fantasy. Sheepishly, Caffrey told me that evening that the arrival of the ring was an anticlimax. "You know," he said, "there's been so much hoopla about this that you'd almost imagine there'd be a big blast of trumpets and somebody'd holler out 'THE TWO-THOUSAND-DOLLAR DIAMOND RING!' and a bunch of people in uniforms would run up on the porch and hand us the ring. Maybe it'd be lying on a silk pillow." Actually, the ring, in a registered package, was simply delivered by Sykes, the letter carrier, who said, as he handed it to Caffrey, "Here's some of the loot at last." Sykes, a friendly fellow, had been interested in the "jack-pot mail" that Caffrey had been receiving, and he was pleased to be the bearer, at last, of a prize.

Caffrey showed me the mail, which was not volu-minous, considering the widespread publicity he had had. It came to thirty-two letters. All those from strangers started out with congratulations and wound up by asking for something. Most of them asked for the two thou-sand dollars' worth of fruit trees. That was because the Associated Press had sent out a story saying that Caffrey didn't know what to do with them.

Caffrey was puzzled about what to do with the ring, too. Around Wakefield, the solid people do not go in for diamond rings. Besides, Caffrey thought constantly of the tax he would have to pay on his prizes, so he wanted to turn most of his winnings into cash, if possible. He took the ring to W. I. Main, the local jeweller, who "put that thing in his eye," Caffrey said, examined the ring, and announced that the diamond weighed about one and one-half carats, and was white, of good brilliance, and with-out flaws. Main offered the opinion that it might be hon-estly described, as it had been on the radio, as a "two-thousand-dollar ring." When Caffrey asked how much he could get for it, Main said cautiously that twelve hundred dollars was a possibility. He had no idea where Caffrey could actually sell it for that much, though.

Before the rest of "the stuff" arrived, Caffrey wrote to the manufacturers of the products he did not want to keep and asked if they would send him cash instead, even if it amounted to much less than the retail value of the product, but all the replies said that policy forbade the substitution of cash. In the next few months, consequently, it was a good thing for Caffrey that he was a good friend of Joe Brierley; otherwise, the Caffrey home would have been filled with the prizes that he had won. Brierley is head of a Wakefield company that sells agricultural implements, hardware, and building materials, and he let Caffrey put the bulkier prizes in the firm's warehouse.

Among these were the seventy-five hundred cans, or one hundred and seventy-nine cases, of "soup." As a matter of fact, there were seventy-five hundred and twelve cans, or twelve more than announced, and they took up one entire twenty-by-twenty-foot compartment in the warehouse. The Darra-James home workshop (complete with motors), which came in nine large packing cases, also went into the warehouse, and so did the air-conditioning unit, which was as big as a good-sized clothes closet, and the bedroom suite and the dining-room suite and the heating system.

The two-thousand-dollar ring, the thousand-dollar

wrist watch (a lady's watch, embellished with fifteen little rubies and seventeen diamonds), and the other small
prizes were easy to take care of. Caffrey carried them in
the pockets of his jacket when he was attempting to sell
them, and once in a while Mrs. Caffrey would wear the
ring for a few hours, just for fun. "Jane wore it to
the hairdresser's one day," Caffrey said to me, "and the
woman in the next booth said, 'Oh, let me see your stone,
will you?' Jane passed it to her, and the woman held it
up beside her own ring and then said, 'Look, it's nearly
as big as mine!' "

As the stuff piled up, and Caffrey tried to turn it into
cash, he became discouraged. He was suddenly in about
twenty lines of business, with all of which he was wholly
unfamiliar. He was in, to name a few, the diamond-ring
business, the Venetian-blind business, the air-conditioning business, the fruit-tree business, the paint-and-varnish
business, the food business, and the heating business.
Moreover, every prospect was aware of his eagerness to
dispose of the prizes, and therefore showed great reluc-
tance to buy. And few of the prospects failed to say, at
one point or another, "Well, after all, Jim, you got all
these things for nothing, you know."

One businessman of Wakefield offered eight hundred
dollars for the two-thousand-dollar ring. "But then he
talked to his wife," Caffrey told me. "She said that if
she blossomed out with a big diamond ring, people might
think business was mighty good with him and that
he must be making big profits on everything, and he

might lose customers that way. So he didn't buy the ring."

Caffrey made more than twenty trips to Providence, which is thirty miles from Wakefield, to try to dispose of his excess prizes. Having been born in Providence, as well as having been a policeman there, he knew the town well. He said it felt strange to be going around the familiar streets with a thousand-dollar wrist watch in one pocket, a two-thousand-dollar diamond ring in another, invoices for and descriptions of fruit trees and an air-conditioning unit in other pockets, attempting to raise cash.

Calling on some of the more sporty citizens one day, some of the "boys" who keep informed about what goes on at the nearby Narragansett Race Track, Caffrey tried to interest them in the wrist watch. "Little too fancy for us," one of the horsy lads said. "We give the girl friends more conservative stuff than that these days. That's the kind of stuff they used to give them in the old gangster days."

There were times, in late September and October, when Caffrey was abysmally depressed. The difficulty of peddling the prizes was getting him down. "If it weren't for the automobile and the few things we've kept for the house, like the deep freeze and the electric range," he would say sorrowfully, "I'd wish the damned jackpot never happened. And I'm worried more and more every day about taxes."

The automobile had been no problem. He phoned the Somerville, Massachusetts, office of the Ford Motor Company and explained about his interest in a station wagon, and the officials there generously arranged to send both the sedan he had won and a brand-new station wagon to the Ford agency in Wakefield. He could have the station wagon by paying the difference in price. With the accessories he wanted, this difference turned out to be $847. Caffrey sold his Pontiac for $1,500. So, after paying the $847, he had the station wagon and was ahead $653 in cash. The cash was the first he had got out of his winnings, and the station wagon was the rolling apple of his eye. "I spent a couple of hundred out of the six hundred and fifty-three dollars," Caffrey said happily as we took a trial ride in the wagon one day. "I bought three cases of Scotch and sent it to Broekman, at the address you gave me. It certainly doesn't seem much, after what he did for me."

Late in October, the Caffreys made a visit to New York. (By then, I was back living in the city myself and making only occasional visits to Wakefield.) While here, they finally disposed of the thousand-dollar wrist watch. They did so by going to the Fifth Avenue office of the Bulova people and turning it in, in exchange for simpler models. Caffrey was ready to settle for one simple watch for himself and one for his wife, because he had become weary of carrying around the ornate, thousand-dollar watch. The Bulova people, however, had more lavish ideas. "You're entitled to more than those two watches in exchange," an amiable official of the company told him. "Tell you what we'll do. You pick out nine more watches, and we'll send them up to your home in Rhode Island. That all right?" Caffrey told me he couldn't help smiling as he agreed to accept the offer. "So now we've got eleven watches, and only want two," he said.

While in New York, Caffrey thought himself duty-bound to do something about another prize — the privilege, to him embarrassing, of having his portrait painted in oil. He manfully telephoned the specified artist, Fred Wright, and was informed that if he would come into the studio and have his picture taken, the artist would work from that. Caffrey expressed his thanks, and then mumbled something about not having time during his brief stay here. At once, he decided that, having gone this far in life without having his portrait painted, he could get along a few more years, and he dropped the burdensome idea entirely.

The main object of the Caffreys' visit, however, was to call at the V.I.P. Service, the company that was to arrange their trip to Nevada. They were told that the trip must be taken before the end of the year, because the hotel that had offered the prize would be closing December 31st. Neither of the Caffreys recalled any such stipulation, but the V.I.P. official with whom they talked insisted that it had been made. It was impossible for Caffrey to get away from the store for two weeks at that time of year. He and Mrs. Caffrey had been figuring that they would go to Nevada in January, February, or March. The V.I.P. Service was unable to consider any of those months, and the Caffreys left New York resigned to the loss of their trip out West. "We thought, that night we won the jackpot, that the Nevada vacation would be one of the nicest prizes of all," Mrs. Caffrey told me.

The next time I saw Caffrey, early in November, he was more cheerful. In the more than two months since Seymour had shouted, "That is absolutely right, Mr. Caffrey, up there in Wakefield, Rhode Island!" I had watched the jackpot take over his life. When he wasn't obliged to be at the store, he was traipsing around Providence looking for buyers for this or that prize. Depending upon his success or lack of it, he was cheery or gloomy. Not loudly, to be sure, because he is a man who presents a serene exterior. "I got all fixed up about the complete steer," he told me now. This prize had been extended to the "Sing It Again" program, and then to Caffrey, by Newton H. Crumley, a hotelkeeper and entrepreneur of Elko, Nevada. He had written to Caffrey offering to send him a check for the value of the "complete steer" if he preferred that to meat. "Crumley said it would be about two hundred and fifty dollars," Caffrey went on. "I had intended to accept the steaks and roasts, but I changed my mind. I wrote and told Crumley O.K. The check came today, for two hundred and fifty dollars exactly. Here it is."

I asked him how much cash he had realized since the day of the jackpot.

"Let me see," he said. "There was the six hundred and fifty-three dollars in cash I had left after getting the station wagon. Then this two hundred and fifty. That'll make nine hundred and three dollars."

This, I said, seemed disappointing, more than two months after J-Day, as he and I had come to call August 28th.

"I often feel that it is, too," Caffrey said. "Remember how it used to be twenty-four thousand dollars? Well, everybody still thinks of it as twenty-four thousand dollars. Everybody except Jane and me. I'm not ungrateful — honest I'm not. It's taking a long while, but they're giving me everything they said they would, all right. Still, I misunderstood a lot of things, and, believe me, that twenty-four-thousand-dollar figure gets hammered into a man's head until, instead of being thankful for the luck that brought him anything at all, he can't help feeling disappointed when what he won keeps shrinking and shrinking."

I told him I thought I understood. For instance, there was lack of interest everywhere in the seventy-five hundred cans of "soup," largely because the stores had regular channels for buying such things. They shied away from "radio prizes," although the food was of standard quality. It was worth a thousand dollars retail, but the best offer he got was two hundred and fifty dollars. Rather than sell it for that, he gave part of it to his church, to be distributed to the needy, and the rest to the South County Hospital.

Early in December, Caffrey's jackpot business began to move a bit faster. "Sold the hope chest," he said jauntily as we met one afternoon for coffee in the Wakefield Diner. "It retails for sixty-nine dollars and ninety-five cents, I found out in Providence. Just sold it to Freddie Arbolino for thirty-five dollars." Freddie Arbolino owns the Mews, the lone cocktail lounge in sedate Wakefield.

"Sold the Venetian blinds," Caffrey announced to me another day. "Never was able to find out how much *they* were worth, but I sold them for ninety dollars, to a fellow here in town. Jane said we didn't need Venetian blinds at our house. Jane doesn't happen to like Venetian blinds."

By the middle of December, Caffrey had sold the electric refrigerator — retail value, $245.95 — to a Narragansett Pier hotel, for $175; the heating system, which was worth $1,000 retail, for $750, to a veteran who was rebuilding a farmhouse; the paint and varnish, to a Wakefield house painter, for $75; the bedroom set, the retail value of which was $239, to a friend in Jerusalem, Rhode Island, for $120; five dozen sheets and pillowcases, to the South County Hospital, for $112.32; and from his "men's wardrobe," three suits similar to some he found selling in Providence for $42.50 each at a sale, to the man who had bought the Pontiac, for $100. (The balance of the wardrobe, a forty-dollar topcoat, he kept for himself.)

"The complete set of luggage, all in Parisian pink, was sold today," Caffrey said jovially a few days later. "It was worth four hundred and fifty-seven dollars, they said in Providence, but I let it go for a hundred and fifty, to a fellow in Lexington, Massachusetts."

"How did you get in touch with him?" I asked.

"Well, when salesmen come into the store to show me goods, and ask about the jackpot, I tell them what I've got to sell, and they keep their eyes open for me while they're traveling around. One of the salesmen made this Lexington deal on the luggage for me."

Bill Beck, the football coach at Rhode Island State College, in Kingston, six miles from Wakefield, bought the home-workshop-complete-with-motors. The retail value was $369, and Caffrey got $250.

"You can see I'm beginning to get some cash out of this thing," Caffrey remarked to me in mid-December. "But I've got all those taxes ahead of me. I still don't know how much they're going to be, but the dope seems to be that they'll come to about one-third of what I realize from selling the stuff."

The Caffreys got some fun out of the things they decided to keep. The television set (retail value $375) worked fine, at times. Caffrey had to pay $128 to have it installed, however. The deep freeze and the washing machine were great things, the Caffreys agreed. Their frozen-food prize, through an arrangement made with the donor, was to be sent in four shipments, at intervals set by Caffrey. The first shipment was thirty-six dozen packages. The freezer would not hold all of them, and Caffrey rented a deep-freeze locker at South County Lockers, at a dollar a month, to keep the overflow. They expected the dishwasher any day, and naturally they would keep that.

"The electric range is perfect, Jane says," Caffrey told me in late December.

"Well, take it all in all, things didn't turn out too badly on this jackpot affair," I ventured.

"You mean the great twenty-four-thousand-dollar jack-pot? Remember when we used to call it that?"

"Yes, but you never really believed it would be that much," I reminded him. "You said the very day after winning it that it wouldn't be — when we were down at the beach."

On February 7th, almost five and a half months after Caffrey had hit the jackpot, I asked him if he had ever sat down and figured out the whole thing; that is, what he had received, its approximate value, what he had realized on the prizes he had sold, and so on.

"To tell you the truth, I did just that today," he said. "What I figured was this. The things we kept were worth thirty-two hundred and nine dollars, retail value. So far, I've taken in twenty-seven hundred and sixty in cash for the things I've sold. I still have the ring, and I'm dicker-ing with a man who may give me seven hundred and fifty dollars for it. The air-conditioning unit is still over in the warehouse, along with the rest of the big stuff I haven't sold or we're not using at the house. I have one prospect who will give me four hundred and fifty dollars for it. Then, there are the well-known fruit trees. They're keeping those down in Louisiana, Missouri, until spring, and they'll send them up here then, they said. Maybe I'll get eight hundred dollars for them, at the ratio I've been selling things at. So, figure it all out — what I've kept, what I've sold, what I'm likely to sell yet — and it adds up to eighty-six hundred and sixty-nine dollars. Take off one third of that for taxes, and you take off twenty-eight hundred and eighty-nine dollars. O.K. That drops the total down to fifty-seven hundred and eighty. Boy! What a hell of a drop from the twenty-four-thousand-dollar jackpot! But what am I kicking about? The television was swell last night. The station wagon is a honey, and the two kids love it as much as Jane and I do. What am I kicking about?"

"You're not kicking," I told Caffrey. "You're just acting like a human being."

PART II

People

1

~~~~~~

Overlooked Lady

~~~~~~

THEY TOOK a census in 1950, as they do every ten years in the United States. This time, I hope they got it right. I happen to know that in the previous census, when they came out with the total of 131,669,275 as the population of the continental United States, it was really at least 131,669,276. I happen to know that they were at least one person below the real total. Know it for a fact.

The reason I know it goes back to the circumstance that Larry Fagan, the city editor of the Pittsburgh *Press*, was, is, and always has been a softy for two classes of people, however hard-boiled he may be in his professional relations with other classes. The two classes are Nice Little Old Ladies and Boys with Dogs.

All kinds of crackpots are always trying to get in to see city editors, so they have a reception desk outside the city room on most papers to keep out the lame-brains. Everybody around the *Press,* however, knew Larry Fagan well enough not to send away anybody who fell into the category of Nice Little Old Lady. It was the same way if a kid and a dog came around. Larry wanted to see them, because he didn't have the heart to turn them away, no matter how tough he was otherwise, as I say.

One day — more than ten years ago, it was — Tony, the head copy boy, came in from the reception desk and spoke to Larry.

"There's a little old lady out there wants to see you, Mr. Fagan," Tony said.

"Gee, Tony, I'm busy," Larry said.

"All right, Mr. Fagan, I'll tell her," Tony said.

"No, no, no. Wait a minute," said Fagan. "Bring her in. I can take a few minutes. Bring her in, Tony. Gee whizz!"

"Yes, sir, Mr. Fagan," Tony said, and he winked at me, without Larry's seeing him.

The person Tony escorted into the city room a few moments later might, I swear, have come from Central Casting if someone had sent in a call for them to send around a Nice Little Old Lady. She was carrying a small handbag with a drawstring at the top; she was only about five feet two; her hair was white and her clothes were dark and nice; and she even wore one of those jabots, a lacy thing at her throat.

There's hardly any provision around city rooms for such visitors, but since there was nobody at the desk next to me, Larry had the old lady sit down there. He threw his stogie away and sat on the desk.

"Yes, Ma'am," Larry said. "Could I do anything to help you?"

"What is your name, sir?" the lady asked in a very nice voice.

"I'm Mr. Fagan — Lawrence J. Fagan," Larry said.

It was the first time I had ever heard him refer to himself as Lawrence J. Fagan, and he knew it, because he glanced at me defiantly. He always said he was Larry Fagan if anybody asked him who he was.

"Mr. Fagan, I like the *Press* very much," the old lady said, quite composed amid the hubbub of the room. "I don't know what I'd do without it every night."

"Thank you, Ma'am," said Larry. "Thank you very much."

"I wondered if you could do something about what has happened," the old lady went on. She smiled. "Or, rather, what has *failed* to happen."

"I'd be glad to do anything I can, Ma'am," Larry replied. Anybody who gets his knowledge of city editors from motion pictures would never believe one of them could be as courteous and genteel as Larry was.

"Well, Mr. Fagan, the census man never came to see me — that's what happened," the old lady said, and she suddenly looked sad.

"I don't quite get what you mean, Ma'am," Larry said.

"Mr. Fagan, you remember you had an article — oh,

you had several articles — in the paper about the census," she said. "They were very interesting. I love the *Press*. You see, I live alone, Mr. Fagan. All my children are in California. Of course, they're all married — but I don't mean to tell you about all that."

"That's all right, Ma'am. What was it you said about the census?" Larry asked.

"Yes, Mr. Fagan, about the census," the old lady said. "One Sunday, you had a long article about the census. It had all the questions the man asks when he comes around to take the census. And it told how the man gets so much for each name he takes down and answers all the questions about."

"Yes, Ma'am, I remember we did have a feature like that," Larry said.

"Well, Mr. Fagan," she said, "I thought I would have everything ready for the man when he came. That would help him get more names that day — whatever day it was he came — because I would be all ready and I wouldn't take too much of his time."

"That was a real nice thing to do, Ma'am," Larry said. He was blinking his eyes too fast. What the old lady had done kind of hit him, I could see that.

"Mr. Fagan, I waited day after day after day, and the man never came," the old lady went on. "Nobody ever came and asked me the questions about the census. I think I've been left out."

"It's all over, the census," Larry said, downcast.

"Yes, Mr. Fagan. There was an item in the *Press* two days ago that said 'Census Completed,' that's what it said.

And the man never came to my house. I must have been left out, don't you think, Mr. Fagan?"

Larry fumbled around with a pencil, then automatically hauled a stogie out of his upper vest pocket, then bethought himself and put it back. "Gee whizz, Ma'am, left out of the census!" he said. "Well, now, I think I can do something. You see, Ma'am, it *is* all over, but I think those government men make some kind of allowance for going back to places they overlooked, maybe."

"I'm sure now they overlooked my house," the old lady said. "And they'll have the count wrong, won't they? Of course, one person won't make much difference, I realize, but I was all ready with the answers and everything."

"Tell you what I'll do, Ma'am," said Larry. "I'll notify the government about this, and I believe they'll send a man up to your place and fix things up right. Could you give me the address?"

"Oh, yes, Mr. Fagan," the old lady said, very much relieved. She gave Larry the address, which was in a decent, quiet part of town. She got up from the chair, and Larry went all the way out to the reception desk with her.

When he came back, he was chewing a stogie and he came over to my desk. "How do you like that?" he said. "Left out of the census! They count every cluck, every lousy heel, every gangster, pimp, and God knows what, and then they leave out a nice old lady like that! My God! Left out of the census, even!"

*   *   *

Larry wasted no time. That afternoon, he got Pete Botsford, one of his best reporters, and he gave him the assignment.

"Rig up some kind of a big book like a census book," he told Pete. "Get that Sunday feature we had with all the census questions in it. Have one of the girls in the front office type out all those questions, so it won't look like out of the paper."

"Yes, Larry. Then what?" Pete asked.

"Go up to this old lady's house and make out you're a government man — census man," Larry said. "Ask her all the questions and put down the answers. Look official as hell. Get the idea? Then come back here. That's all you have to do."

"Sure. But I *don't* get the idea," Pete said.

"Jeez, I forgot to tell you what it was all about," Larry said. "This old lady was left out of the census. Imagine being left out of the census, a nice old lady?"

He told Pete all about the visitor he had had, and Pete went out to the old lady's house that afternoon and did as he was told.

"She gave me a cup of tea," he told Larry when he came back with all the questions.

"Nice old lady," Larry said. "She seem satisfied?"

"Tickled to death," Pete said.

"You can throw away those questions and all, Pete," Larry said. "I suppose we wasted some time, but what the hell. What the hell."

2

~~~~~~

Slightly Crocked

~~~~~~

JOHN FOWLER sat on the porch of the beach club at the end of the day, thoroughly pleased with himself and his surroundings and life in general.

During the afternoon he had been in swimming three times, and he had been to the bar just enough times. That is, he had maintained a proper balance — the sting of the rye at the bar and then, a few minutes later, the salt water washing away the taste of the rye. Each swim had made him feel that he had canceled out the harm of the whisky and kept the fun of it. For a man who tended to go overboard on drinking, that was the ideal, seldom achieved.

So, sitting alone on the porch, he looked at the sea gulls walking purposefully at the edge of the water and thought to himself what good luck he had had with whisky and waves that day. He was pleased that he could think of one dignified old sea gull as a bishop, and the sea gull who followed in matronly style as the bishop's lady. Without the drinks, thought Fowler, I wouldn't see a couple of old sea gulls in that light, and if I did, why, I'd be ashamed of it. They *do* look like a bishop and his lady, he said to himself.

From up the beach there came a lovely young girl riding along the sands on a horse. Fowler thought that that was a fine sight. The girl wore overalls rolled up to her knees and a gay shirt, and she sat nice and loose on the horse, with her back straight, as she should. Against the background of the sea, horse and girl were perfect. Fowler watched them as they approached and then passed him and finally passed out of sight, and again he was warmly delighted at his awareness in the twilight. He was thankful that he was slightly crocked.

Just then some music drifted down the easy sunset wind. Fowler knew that it was canned music from the carnival, a quarter of a mile, maybe three eighths, down the road in back of the club. (He had passed the carnival lot early that afternoon, walking from the hotel to the club. They were just putting up the stuff then — a Ferris wheel, a merry-go-round, a half-dozen booths, a sadly small menagerie.) The distance softened the brazen crackle of the loud-speaker, and the music was clear and admirable to Fowler. A march tune, "Under the Double Eagle," was being played, and as Fowler listened, he looked at the darkening sea and beat time gently with one hand. He kept his feet up on the porch railing. He didn't want any more drinks. The sea gulls, the girl on the horse, the music borne on the wind — everything was perfect.

"Da-*da*-da-de-da, da-de-*da*" went the tune on the air, very gay and beckoning, and Fowler took his feet down from the rail and was surprised to note that he was speaking out loud, but not very loud, to himself. "I guess I'll go to the carnival," he heard himself saying. "Just take a walk there for a look at it."

He nodded in friendly but slightly aloof style to a few friends in the club bar as he passed through without stopping, on his way to the outside door, and in a minute or two he was out on the road. There's a pleasant walk ahead, he thought. And it was, with the darkness coming down, the sound of the sea on his left, and the growing sound of the carnival ahead, and a nightfall scent of sea, and sweet grass, and — oh, yes — iodine, over it all.

I wouldn't have thought of that iodine without the drinks all day, Fowler thought, and quite proudly. The sea is full of iodine, and the seaweed, too, and not everybody knows that.

Fowler turned into the carnival lot, and the trampled-down grass felt springy under his feet. The brightness of the spottily lighted booths, merry-go-round, Ferris wheel, and the popcorn stand was dazzling. "In a brave little way," Fowler murmured. Again, as a few times before in his usually steady life, he felt a childlike admiration for people of carnivals and the courage they have in going always to unknown towns.

It had been more than an hour, nearly an hour and a half, since his last drink, but Fowler was still just right when he stopped at the last booth on the lot. What caught his eye there was the shining stacks of silver dollars. There were two such stacks, each as high as a man's hand from finger tip to wrist, and they were standing there on the table at the rear of the booth.

The guy running the little stand presided over the dollars, and he was running a kind of dice game. How many dollars, Fowler wondered as he stood there a minute with other carnival visitors, watching the play of the game. He tried to count them, but the coins blurred in the light. Was it twenty-four in each pile? Hard to count, because the carnival man kept jingling the top coins up and down in the stacks as he talked to the small group playing the game.

He was a tough-looking guy, but Fowler saw a kind of gaiety in his eyes, a look of what-the-hell-difference-does-anything-make.

It was a simple game they were playing, simpler than a crap game. The players put their quarters, half-dollars, dimes, or, rarely, dollars on squares on the surface of a counter which had built-up sides. After all the bets were down, the guy threw the dice for a point. If he threw an eight, all those who later threw higher than an eight, on their turn to throw, were paid off. Some winners got silver dollars, others got smaller coins. Those who threw an eight or less lost their money. The guy won on the ties. He got his percentage that way. Also, he threw a lot of nines, and they were hard to beat.

Fowler was playing almost before he knew it, and winning. He had a handful of silver dollars in no time, maybe fourteen, and he was happy at how much more like money they felt than bills. And every silver dollar was new, untarnished. That was part of the lure, the way the dollars gleamed.

Fowler lost a couple of times, then won again. He was jingling the dollars in his hands when the guy said, "Wait a minute, boys, wait a minute."

The guy was looking down at a little kid, maybe six or seven years old, who had strayed around to the back of the counter, where only the guy was supposed to be. He halted the game, leaned over, and spoke to the kid.

"Here, Johnny," he said, "go on over to the merry-go-round." He handed the kid a dime. Then he smiled and said, "*Is* your name Johnny? Anyway, beat it to the merry-go-round, like a good kid. This is no place for you, Johnny."

The boy looked up and grinned, and stayed where he was. The guy looked at Fowler, who was a bigger, older man than any of the other players, and shrugged and laughed.

At that instant, the drinks, and the fun of the waves, and the pleasant walk down the road all surged up in Fowler. He took a silver dollar and spun it in the air over the table to the kid, so that it almost landed in his hand. "Go on to the merry-go-round!" he said.

The carnival guy looked at him, and there was a kind

of gay and reckless challenge in his eyes. "Wait a minute!" he said. And he reached to the pile of dollars, picked one off, and tossed it to the kid. Then he looked at Fowler and grinned.

Fowler threw the kid another dollar. The kid scrambled wildly for it, picked it up, and stared at both men.

The guy threw him another dollar. "I'll keep it up as long as you do, Mac!" he said, and Fowler felt then that the guy was from New York, where the name of every encountered stranger is Mac or Chief.

The contest went on — a silver dollar from Fowler, a silver dollar from the guy, the kid scrambling, the dollars glinting in the air, dollar, dollar, dollar, and the kid was dizzy with delight, both hands full of coins.

I think that's nine from me, thought Fowler, and he saw he had four more. "I quit," he said.

"I'll always top you," said the guy, not surly but confident. "Here, Johnny, go to the merry-go-round." He threw the kid another dollar, then still another. Then he turned back to the players. "All right, boys," he said as he picked up the dice again. "Let's get going. All you got to do is beat me."

Fowler turned to watch the amazed kid, clinging to his wondrous handfuls of bright silver dollars and running through the crowd. He saw him stop before a man and woman, somber folk who were staring idly around, as townspeople do at carnivals. Their eyes popped as they saw their son and the dollars. Then they grabbed him and hustled away — all three.

Fowler threw the rest of his silver dollars on the counter, pleased to let them go. On his turn at the dice, he lost them.

Wasn't it a great day, thought Fowler as he left the brightly lighted lot and started walking back to the club. Everything was just right. I think I could stand another drink now. But I got to be careful. I don't want to spoil everything.

3

Mrs. Carmody's Store

Mrs. Carmody's corner store was the kind that widows used to run in all the little towns in the East. Here and there you'll still find such a store, but Mrs. Carmody was running hers thirty or forty years ago.

The store sold *Pluck and Lucks* and potatoes (hardly ever any more than half a peck at a time), Laura Jean Libbey novels, "16–1" chocolate bars, transfer pictures to make pseudo-tattoos on the back of a kid's hand, kindling wood tied into small bundles with very hairy cord, Clark's O.N.T. thread, cigars and tobacco, Copenhagen snuff, kerosene in small quantities, nonpareils, *Young Wild Wests* and *Work and Wins*, and the Lord knows what else.

The *Pluck and Lucks*, the *Young Wild Wests*, and

the *Work and Wins* were five-cent story books that came out every week. They were hung on a wire strung across the back of Mrs. Carmody's small show window, so that the highly colored front pages could lure readers from the street.

Mrs. Carmody had two children, John and his younger, quieter brother, William. John, who was just turning nine, had his troubles with the *Young Wild Wests* and the other stories. He read all of them, but he had to do so without cutting the pages, which were uncut at the top. As soon as they were cut, they became secondhand *Pluck and Lucks* or *Young Wild Wests,* or whatever they were, and they were then worth only two-for-five. So young John developed a curious skill at holding the novels with the pages lifted up as far as they would go, uncut, and reading way up into the corners in that manner. It sounds as if it would be hard on the eyes, but it didn't seem to hurt his at all.

The nonpareils — pronounced "nonperells" — were a kind of candy, just as the "16–1s" were. The nonpareils were dark, shaped about like a button, and had a lot of tiny white dots imbedded in them. The "16–1s" were named, probably, after the political slogan of a William Jennings Bryan campaign a few years before. The "16–1s" were one cent apiece; nonpareils were five for a cent; butterballs, which were not butter but yellow candy, were four for a cent; licorice shoelaces were two for a cent; fried eggs were one cent each. They weren't fried eggs but candy in a tiny tin frying pan, the candy colored and fashioned to look like a fried egg in the pan.

With each pan came a tiny spoon. Smart kids were aware the spoon had very sharp edges. The tin from which spoon and pan were made was not very heavy, and the handle of the pan or the whole spoon, or both, was almost sure to bend awkwardly when you tried to hold them and peck the candy out of the pan, a trifle at a time.

There was a whole showcase full of these candies. Young John, who helped out a little — very little — in "waiting on" in the store, knew the prices of all the candies. Occasionally, however, he would sell five butterballs for a cent, instead of four, and perhaps four montevideos, if he knew the kid who was buying the candy. He never did, at that time, get a clear picture of profits and all that, or realize how small a gain each sale meant in the little store. He was too harum-scarum to care, anyway, although Mrs. Carmody had tried to explain to him about those things, especially about when to give the candy out in a bag and when not to.

"If they buy one cent's worth, or two or three or even four cents' worth," Mrs. Carmody often told him, "just hand them the candy, nicely, of course, in their hand. If they buy five cents' worth or more, put it in a bag. Those bags cost money, John, and we'll lose if you don't do what I tell you."

John paid small attention to that or to most other things his mother told him. Mrs. Carmody herself was expert in selling the candies and she had hard-and-fast rules about "merchandising" them, as they would say now in the big stores. One of her rules was that a kid was allowed just so much time to stand in front of the candy case, trying to make up his mind what to buy. This permissible period of indecision was ticked off by a metronome in Mrs. Carmody's mind. At the end of the allotted time she would walk away without a word, and the kid, who was sure to come to a decision an instant later, would have to stand and wait a while, painfully anxious to get the candy.

Of course, there was never any announcement or any signs up about these house rules, but practically everybody knew about them. And customers took their four cents' worth of candy in their hands, or waited for the bag when they bought five cents' worth or more.

The little store was busy most of the time. People started going to it out of sympathy, and then they got used to going there and they kept on trading there for small things. Mrs. Carmody's husband had died when John was only two years old and his brother was only a few months old. Relatives had chipped in, maybe two hundred dollars altogether, to add to what was left of the insurance money after the funeral, and with this money they set up the store for the widow. She and the two children lived in the back of the store, and a bell on the end of a wire over the door rang when anybody came in. Mrs. Carmody would then come out from the back living quarters, if she was there, and wait on the customer. After a while she was able to take wonderful care of the two children, even on the small profits of the place.

Father Maurice Murphy, who was a steady customer, said she took too good care of them. He said she was spoiling them, especially John. "You do too well by those children, Mary," Father Maurice often said to Mrs. Carmody. "You give them too much and you keep them too clean and too well dressed, especially himself."

By "himself" he meant John. Now that the father of the family was dead, John was referred to as "himself," although he was just becoming nine. In families of Mrs. Carmody's nationality, they always used the word "himself" like that, whether they were in America or Ireland. It was a habit, meaning that "himself" is the oldest male in the family. "Himself" always got the best of everything there was in the house. And he also got spoiled for the rest of his life.

For example, at the Carmodys', when there was mashed potatoes at supper, Mrs. Carmody would make a mound of them on a plate, and at the top she'd make a small indentation, into which she'd put a big chunk of butter to melt. When the two children and herself were seated, she would scoop off the first big spoonful of potatoes in such a way that the melted butter ran down all in one place. And that delicious buttery portion always went to "himself," while the younger brother looked on enviously. The little brother must have hated to see that happen time and time again but he wasn't the oldest man and nothing could be done about it.

When John got to be eight years old, he was allowed to wait on, once in a while, at the tobacco showcase. That was the more manly part of the store, on the right-hand side as you came in. Roughly, the right-hand side of the store was male, the left-hand female. There were five showcases in all — two on each side, running from the front toward the back of the store, and the fifth running partly across the store at the back, making a sort of square "U," with the street door in the opening. On the right, the male side, the first showcase was for tobacco, cigars, and cigarettes, although there were not one tenth or even one twentieth as many kinds of cigarettes as there are now; the second showcase on the right had small toys for boys, like tops, marbles, and those transfer pictures. On the left as you entered, the first showcase had cakes and pies; the second had an assortment of ribbons and women's stuff like that. The candy case was the one that ran partly across the store.

It was a kind of coming of age for John to be allowed to wait on tobacco customers. His mother, however, tried to steer him away from selling cigarettes, because in those days they were associated with a fast life. There weren't so many kinds of them, in Mrs. Carmody's, anyway — just Sweet Caporals and some called Perfections, in a red package, and some twenty-for-a-nickel brands, like Meccas and Cycles. Chewing tobacco was the popular item, and there was a simple device, a blade in a fixed frame, with a handle, to cut the chewing tobacco — B.L. and Piper Heidsieck, or whatever the tobacco was — into various-priced chunks, into ten-cent pieces and five-cent pieces. Piper Heidsieck was for the more exquisite trade; B.L. was democratic stuff.

John had a perilous pastime at the tobacco counter, a

trick to be done only when Mrs. Carmody was in the back. There was a cigar cutter on one end of the counter. It had to be wound up, for it had a quick-acting spring inside. You pushed the end of the cigar into a tiny hole, a blade leaped across the hole, and neatly cut the sealed end of the cigar. John's trick was to shove the tip of his forefinger in the machine, far enough to make the spring work, and then yank his finger out before it got cut. It was dangerous, and such a feat as only somebody called "himself" would try.

Father Maurice caught him at it one day, but didn't stop him. He just watched and said, "Yuh, you *would* be doing something like that." He seemed to half approve of the trick.

Father Maurice had tricks of his own, such as making the two kids get all messed up on purpose. As he had told Mrs. Carmody, he thought she kept them too clean to be natural. They were always spotless and that irked Father Maurice.

Just behind the counter that ran across the back of the store, and before you got into the living quarters, there was a small coal stove. It was useful for making a cup of tea. There was a coal hod beside it. And if Father Maurice came in and Mrs. Carmody was in the back, he'd tell her to stay there and he'd watch the store. Then he would call the two children. "Look," he'd say, "go get this money and you can have it." And he would drop two or three pennies away down in the coal hod. John and his brother would dig into the coal, and pretty soon their hands and faces would be grimy, their clean clothes blackened. "Now you look like regular kids," Father Maurice would say, and discreetly slip out of the store.

"Himself" usually got the pennies. He got the first big possession either one of the two children had, too. That was the day of his ninth birthday. Mrs. Carmody gave him a bicycle. It was a stupendous gift. It had to be bought out of money scrupulously saved by Mrs. Carmody, and certainly she had had to plan it way ahead. She had hated to see "himself" always trying to borrow a bike for a brief ride from one of the few kids in the neighborhood who had bikes. But he was always doing that.

To get "himself" a bike of his own, Mrs. Carmody first had to have a long talk with Jim Berry, the bicycle man. The bike had to be of a smaller size than the standard, because John was only nine and most bikes in those days were made for bigger kids. So Jim Berry had to send away for it quite a while in advance. When it came, Berry brought it to the store at night, after John had been sent to bed. It was a red bike and it even had a lamp that used calcium carbide. Berry showed Mrs. Carmody how the lamp worked. The chemical was grayish stuff that was carried in a receptacle fastened on the bike. Another receptacle fed water into the calcium when a switch was turned on. That made gas, which flowed through a tube into the lamp and through a Y-shaped outlet, where it could be lighted. The whole thing smelled very scientific and slightly dangerous. Mrs. Carmody was sure John would like it. Mrs. Carmody gave Mr. Berry a part payment on the bike and agreed to pay him a dollar seventy-five every two weeks until it was paid for. They hid the bike that night in the store.

The next morning, John's birthday, John came out of the back of the store to fold the papers. That was an early-morning job for his mother, and he usually helped a little at it. They would fold the papers just before they unlocked the front door and pile the different papers at certain places on the counter, so that people hurrying to work could rush in, grab their favorite paper almost without looking, and quickly go along. It was the custom to pay for them at the end of the week. Mrs. Carmody used to open the store at twenty minutes to six and she never kept it open after ten o'clock at night. It was a long day, but then there were moments of rest when things got quiet and she could have a cup of tea.

As John started to fold the papers, he looked idly across the store. There was the bike, leaning against one counter. He dropped the paper and ran over.

"It's mine! It's my birthday!" he said, grabbing the handle bars. They felt just right. "Hurry up, Mama! Open the door!"

He couldn't get the bike out fast enough into the street. The pedal on one side caught for a moment on his mother's apron as she unlocked the door and then held it open for him to take the bicycle out. While she was looking down to see if the apron was torn, off he went on the bike, up the street. She didn't even see him start his first trip on the great gift. The apron wasn't torn and

Mrs. Carmody went back to the job of folding the papers by herself.

It was summer and there was no school to go to, so John rode the bike all that morning. He didn't want any breakfast, he had said, hollering over his shoulder as he rode by the store. His mother made him eat something at noontime, after shouting at him to come in as he went by again.

He wheeled the bike all the way into the back part of the store, where they lived. In between bites of what his mother had put on the table, John pulled down the curtains on the windows. That didn't make it black dark, but dark enough so he could switch on the calcium lamp on the bike and light it. It smelled up the place, but nobody stopped him from doing it. He hated to turn off the lamp, but he did before he pushed the bicycle out into the daylight again.

He couldn't get enough of the bike that day, and he thought it would never get dark so the lamp could be used. He rode everywhere around the neighborhood, and into strange neighborhoods, into which he had seldom, if ever, been on foot. Always he'd circle back to the store, then start out again.

At about four o'clock, John was standing up rakishly on the pedals, riding the bike through a short cut. That was a path through a vacant lot. Quite suddenly, he had to stop and get off, because there were two women right ahead of him and they took up all the path. He did not want to risk riding the new bike around them, because there might be broken glass in the grass beside the path and he wouldn't see it. He got off with a flourish and, walking, pushed the bike. The women paid no particular attention to him. They merely glanced around, saw it was some kid or other and a bike, and went on talking.

"Isn't she the old miser, though, that Mrs. Carmody!" one of the women said to the other.

John heard her say it and the bike wobbled. The front wheel went over a stone and bumped, and John's face stung, and he almost could not hold the handle bars.

"Look at the way I have to carry home this candy!" the woman went on. "I happened to have just four pennies and I bought that much. To bring home to the children."

"Yes, yes," the other woman said, nodding.

"And would Mrs. Carmody give me a bag to carry it in? Not her! Not that one! No wonder she has all kinds of money. If ever there was a miser, that Mrs. Carmody is one."

John was in quick fear the women would turn and recognize him, and he was shaking and swallowing. He had an awful job turning the bicycle around and walking back to the beginning of the short cut, toward the store. He was stumbling and sick. He knew he had heard what he did, but he couldn't believe that anybody had said it.

He was still trembling when he climbed on the bike at the end of the vacant lot. The wind helped to cool his face when he raced as fast as he could to the store. Outside the store, he hastily tried to lean the bike against the curb, with one pedal catching the curb. He did it so quickly and badly it started to fall, but he caught it in time, fixed the pedal firmly, and ran into the store.

On his last two steps before the door, he seemed to catch hold of himself. He hurried to his mother, in back of the counter.

"Mama! Mama!" he said. "Thank you for the bike. Thank you very much."

4

Müller with an Umlaut

MALLORY walked along the avenue toward Hollywood Boulevard and came to the drugstore. He had the New York habit of glancing at headlines on a newspaper stand, and doing so now, he saw one headline in the Los Angeles *Times*. It said:

MERCURY HITS
RECORD HIGH

He stopped and peeked at the first paragraph and found out that the new record, for this date in January, was eighty-nine.

In New York, he would have bought the newspaper. Here in Los Angeles, he had given up trying to read the newspapers. No matter how he tried, they never grew less unfamiliar to him.

He continued down the avenue, toward Hollywood Boulevard. Eighty-nine was too high for the dead of winter. Mallory felt slightly angry at the sun, which was shining warmly down upon him. It should not, in all decency, be shining that brightly this time of year, Mallory thought resentfully.

Nevertheless, it was, and for a moment he thought he might as well give in to it, make the best of it. Thousands of people spent their lives trying to make enough money to get to California for the winter, yet here he was hating the sunshine they came for. O.K.

He sat on a bench near the curb, one of those put there for people waiting for buses. For a few minutes he let the sun hit him in the face, just as it used to, in the proper summer, on beaches in Connecticut or in Rhode Island. Hardly three minutes had passed before he got restless. He looked around and noticed that the bench he was sitting on bore the advertisement of a mortuary. Gee, there are a lot of ads about death around this part of the world, he thought, also resentfully. He got off the bench and started down the avenue again.

Across the way, he saw a sign, "JERRIE'S." That kind of name on a bar reminded him a little of New York, but in New York he was sure it would have been spelled the simple way, "JERRY'S."

Odd thing about California, Mallory thought, as he crossed the street toward Jerrie's: they boast about the sunshine, and they do a lot of the boasting while they're sitting at midday in the darkest corners of cocktail bars. All the bars seem dark, and in them Californians hide from the sun.

Jerrie's was not wholly dark, Mallory discovered when he stepped inside. Up near the open door, a patch of light came to the edge of the bar, and he sat on a stool in the bright patch. It was only twenty minutes to noon and there were only eight people in the place.

Mallory was glad to note that the place was not too different from a New York saloon in appearance. It was not too chromiumed up or too red-leathered. And he noticed that nobody besides himself was in the sunlit fragment of the bar. The other customers were in the back, in the dark.

Still further back, beyond the customers, the bartender was eating from a dish on the bar. He was eating in determined fashion, but he looked up when Mallory came in and sat down.

Mallory wanted to be decent. So he held up his hand in gesture to the bartender, trying to indicate to him not to interrupt his breakfast. Just the same, the bartender flung down his fork and walked up loudly toward Mallory.

"Yes, sir?" he asked.

"Bottle of beer," said Mallory. "What kind you got?"

"Acme, East Side, oh God, two or three others," the bartender said, very tired.

"That East Side don't mean New York, does it?" asked Mallory. He felt silly for saying it.

"No," said the bartender, and he grabbed the inside rail of the bar, hanging on to it. Had a little hang-over himself, probably, Mallory thought.

"Got any Pabst, names like that?" Mallory asked.

"Yuh, I got Pabst," the bartender said, and moved down the bar. He came back in a moment, opening the bottle on the way. He put it and a glass in front of Mallory, who tipped the glass and poured the beer into it skillfully, so there wasn't too much head on the beer.

"I didn't want to break in on your breakfast," Mallory said while he poured the beer.

"Ah, that's all right," said the bartender, and he stood there with the brazenly patient look of a bartender waiting to be paid for a drink.

"How much?" Mallory asked. "You from the East? You sound like a guy from the East. They sound different, somehow."

"New Jersey," said the bartender. "Thirty cents."

Mallory took thirty cents from the pocket of his plaid jacket.

"Here," he said. "Where in New Jersey? Whereabouts in New Jersey?"

"Cedar Grove," the bartender said. "It's near Newark. Thanks."

The bartender returned to the far end of the bar and resumed eating. Between him and Mallory, the other customers sat, talking to each other. With a forkful of food in his right hand, the bartender spoke past them, the length of the bar, addressing Mallory. "Was you ever in Newark?" he asked. "I know you was never in Cedar

Grove. But Newark, maybe?" He mopped some bread on the plate.

Mallory drank some of the beer. "No, I don't ever remember being in Cedar Grove," he said, loud enough to carry the bar's length. "Seems like a name I heard, though. I was in Newark the night Dutch Schultz got killed there. Not *when* he was killed. I got there after he was killed. Remember when he got killed?"

"He did get killed in Newark," the bartender said. "I remember that, yuh. Dutch Schultz. Old Dutch Schultz. These people don't even know who the hell we're talking about."

Mallory didn't say anything.

The bartender put down his fork and walked up toward him, with tremendous leisure, although one of the people at the bar wanted something. He leaned on the bar, across from Mallory. Neither one of them said anything for a moment; then the bartender spoke. "You lonesome out here?" he asked. "I been here since 1934."

"I been here three months yesterday," Mallory said. "Yes, I get lonesome. There don't seem to be anyplace to go here, no place to walk, even."

"Did you used to go to the fights in the Garden on Friday nights?" the bartender asked sadly. "Back in New York?"

"Yes, I used to, sometimes," Mallory said. "What's your name? My name is Mallory — M-a-l-l-o-r-y. Harry Mallory."

The bartender wiped his right hand on his apron, reached over the bar, and shook hands. "My name is

Müller," he said. "Fred. It ought to be Frederick. That's too fancy, though." He laughed.

"It sounds as if it might be M-u-l-l-e-r, with an umlaut over the 'u,'" said Mallory. For an instant he was proud of his few months of German in high school thirty years ago.

"I be goddammed," said the bartender. "That's the way it is, with an umlaut. Two dots. None of these bozos out here would ever know that." He gestured disdainfully toward the other customers.

"Oh, some of them might," said Mallory. "They're not all dumb out here. It's nothing important, anyway."

"I didn't say they was dumb," said the bartender. "Some of the nicest guys in the world out here. But they ain't like in the East. Nothing is. Ever go to the fights here?"

"Once," said Mallory, "but they didn't seem like regular fights."

"See?" the bartender said. "That's what I mean. Don't seem real. You used to go to the Garden, huh?"

"Sometimes," said Mallory. "Give me another Pabst."

The bartender hurried down the bar, got the Pabst, and brought it back. He passed three people knocking for service with half-dollars on the bar. "Jeez, I get lonesome out here," he said. "None of these things they go for around here seem to mean anything — movies, sunshine, nothing. The sun oughtn't to be shining like this in the dead of winter, should it? I don't know why it makes you lonesome for New York. It does, though."

Mallory took out some silver as the bartender poured the beer.

"Keep your dough in your pocket," the bartender said.

Mallory put his dough in his pocket. "Yeah," he said. "The sunshine makes a guy lonesome for New York. The paper said it was eighty-nine here yesterday."

5

~~~~~~

Yellow–Ball–in–the–Side

~~~~~~

For YEARS NOW, the Brunswick-Balke-Collender people and other outfits that manufacture pool tables have been conducting a campaign to take the sense of shadiness out of pool playing. They send Charlie Peterson and other gentlemanly top-notch pool players around the country to prep schools and colleges and to pasteurized pool halls in key cities in an effort to remove from the public mind the notion that there is something sinful about shooting pool.

Pool is a nice game, and it would be nicer if they did manage to wring the sin out of it, so this campaign is probably praiseworthy enough. But as far as I am concerned, the Brunswick-Balke-Collender people and the rest of them might as well give up. Long as I live, when

I'm playing pool, I am going to feel that I am not putting in my time in the most wholesome of ways. I wouldn't feel a hundred per cent pure while playing pool if I were playing in the cellar of the Vatican.

This feeling goes back a long way. When I was only six years old and getting acquainted with numbers in school, the sign painted on the window of the ground-floor poolroom in our neighborhood said, "POOL — 2½ CENTS A CUE."

This puzzled me very much, because I couldn't figure out how the half cent could be paid. For a while, I tried to dope out this problem for myself, without asking anybody, but I was unable to do so. So one day I asked my mother about it. My mother was a widow who ran a little candy store at the corner of Lawrence and Elm Streets in a small New England town, and we lived in back of the store — my mother, my younger brother, and I.

"Mama, are there any half cents?" I asked her in the store. "How do you pay for anything that's a half a cent?"

"You know there aren't any half cents," my mother said. "You've waited-on in the store enough to know that. Is it something in school? Why do you ask me about such a silly thing?"

"It says on the window of the poolroom — it says, 'Two and a half cents a cue,'" I explained. "How do they pay that — Joe Shine and those men that go in there?"

In an instant, I could see that I had asked something wrong, something that alarmed my mother.

"You just let Joe Shine and those men go in there, and you never mind what it says on that old poolroom window," my mother said. The way she said it made me aware for the first time that there was something pretty bad about going into the poolroom.

It was a long time before I got the half-cent thing straightened out, because our conversation was shunted off right then and there, and I don't remember when or how, finally, I discovered that one person doesn't play pool by himself, and as long as there were two, it would be two times two and a half cents, or a nickel.

It was also a long time — something like ten or eleven years after that — before I was able to go into the poolroom. All those years, it was an unspoken ambition of mine to be able to go in there. It was illegal to have minors in poolrooms, but the man who ran the poolroom, an Armenian named Alfred Avakian, put a kind of rubbery interpretation on the word "minor." To him, the question of who was a minor and who wasn't hinged largely on pants. Males in short pants were minors; males in long pants tended to be of legal poolroom age. To be sure, a boy couldn't prance into the poolroom the very first day he changed from wearing short pants to wearing long pants. For admission to the poolroom, the pants had to have a little age on them. In those days, kids wore knee pants until they were fifteen or sixteen, depending on their physique, and a boy was usually pretty near seventeen before he could go into the poolroom with any confidence that he would be permitted to stay there and to play.

When I slipped furtively into the poolroom a few times during my early long-pants days, I was put out by Alfred. There came a day, however, when I got by with it, and there came a time when I was able to play a tidy little game of pool. Never got to be a "shark," like a select few of the fellows who had been in my class in Caesar's *Gallic Wars,* but I got to be better than fair. Thinking of it now, I believe I was more than a little swell-headed about my pool. I must have been.

One day, I was sitting in the tiny parlor in back of the store reading a book called *Shorthand Tom.* This book was about a young fellow who made great strides in the fields of business, adventure, and romance by reason of his superb skill at writing shorthand. There was one part where Shorthand Tom helped to capture a gang who had contraband on a ship, but I don't recall how writing shorthand worked into that part of the story. Anyway, I was both reading and toying with the notion of studying only shorthand — dismissing all other subjects as extraneous and skipping college — when my mother came in and asked me to do an errand. I was often lolling in the living quarters back of the store while my mother was working quite hard in the front part, and my mother was indulgent about that.

"This is the first of the month," my mother said, "so I want to pay Dixie Sullivan the insurance money."

"Ma, let me finish this, will you, Ma?" I said, meaning the life of Shorthand Tom.

"Oh, there's no hurry, John," my mother said. "It's

early, and Dixie Sullivan's will be open all afternoon, until six o'clock."

"I'm almost finished, Ma," I said.

"All right," she said. "Then I'll give you the money and the bill, and you can go downstreet and pay it. I could wait until the tenth, the way some of them do, but I always pay right on the first of the month, and then nobody can say I'm slow pay."

"All right, Ma. Soon as I'm finished, I'll go," I said.

"See, it says on the bill, 'Payment due when bill is presented, or tenth of month at latest,'" my mother said, and I glanced at the bill she showed me. It was for ten dollars, a quarterly insurance payment.

My mother was always good to me, but she was extra good that day. After she had given me Dixie Sullivan's insurance bill and ten dollars with which to pay it, she gave me a quarter for myself. I had said that I'd like to go to the Premier, the movie house, while I was downstreet.

"Why don't you have a nice glass of Moxie before you start?" she said. "It's a hot day, and it's good for you."

My mother opened a bottle of Moxie from the store's supply, poured me a glass, and said, "Good for the nerves, eh, John?" She laughed. "Isn't that what they say about Moxie?"

On my way down past the Common to Dixie Sullivan's office, on Essex Street, I met Danny McCafe. Danny, who was my age, is the only fellow I ever met who had the name McCafe, which was pronounced as if it were spelled McKayfe.

"What do you say we go to the Majestic?" Danny asked me. The Majestic was absolutely the fanciest poolroom in town. The men who racked up the balls there wore white coats, and there were two billiard tables, as well as about twelve pool tables.

"I was going to the movies, after I do an errand," I said.

"We could shoot a little yellow-ball," Danny said. "How about a nice little game of yellow-ball-in-the-side? Got any money?"

"Oh, I got some money," I said. "Only, I was going to the Premeer. But I'll shoot you a game."

So we went to the Majestic. I had it in for Danny McCafe a little. He beat me around Alfred Avakian's quite often, but I was improving fast, and I hadn't played him for some time.

We played the first game for a dime, and I beat him. Yellow-ball is a game where whoever knocks the one-ball, which is yellow, into the right-hand side pocket wins the game. The right-hand side of a pool table is the side on your right when you're standing at the end of the table that has the manufacturer's nameplate on it — in this case, at the Majestic, Brunswick-Balke-Collender.

I beat Danny McCafe two games for a dime, and I beat him two more games, all in a row, for a quarter each, and I don't think to this day that he was giving me a come-on and lying down on me. Playing for a quarter was not common with us, but in the Majestic we tended to play for more than we played for in Alfred Avakian's crummy joint.

We worked up, finally, to playing for a dollar a game, and I remember that by that time about five people were watching us. I felt pretty big, even when I was losing. In the end, I lost the ten dollars insurance money.

"Now I *got* to do that errand!" I said chokingly to McCafe while I was paying him my last dollar. "Jeez, it's nearly six o'clock."

I didn't wait for Danny to go out of the Majestic with me. I almost ran out, in a hurry to be alone. I was appalled by what I had done. More than that, I was terrified about how to get out of it.

It must have been nearly seven o'clock when I finally went into the public library, which was open until eight, and went to a corner, between the bookshelves, where there was a table and nobody around. In big letters I painfully wrote on the bill, "Rec'd Paym't, Dixie Sullivan."

That's what I gave my mother when I got back to the store. I gave it to her quick, before she asked for it. I worried that night about whether I should have waited until she asked for the receipted bill. Awake, worrying, I remembered all the other times I had paid that kind of bill, and it seemed, in my memory, that each time I had stuck the receipt in my pocket someplace, and when I had come back to the store, my mother had had to ask for it and I had had to fish in all my pockets before I found it. Did she notice that I had come right into the store and handed it to her, without her asking?

I wondered about that for a long time that night.

In the conscience-tortured days after that, I looked ahead with the greatest fear to the eleventh of the month. That was because I remembered the "tenth of month at latest" that was on Dixie Sullivan's bill. I feared that he would get in touch with my mother precisely on the eleventh and that something terrible would happen.

Nothing did, on the eleventh.

Nor were my theft and forgery laid bare on the twelfth, the thirteenth, or on any of the days that immediately followed them. Then there was a period of relief from anguish when I reasoned that I had until the first of the next month before another bill would come in. Dixie Sullivan, I figured, was being lenient with my mother and would wait until then to remind her of the unpaid insurance premium. I also had a hopeful feeling, during this period, that a miracle would happen — that somehow I would get ten dollars and pay Dixie Sullivan, and nobody would ever know about the disastrous afternoon of pool. The rest of my life, because of those days, I have read in newspapers about trapped embezzlers and I have known in my heart that they, too, waited day after day for the miracle that never happened.

The last night of the month, hope of the miracle had thinned and I hardly slept. The next day, my mother, who wasn't laughing or joking, as she so often was, told me I would have to mind the store for a while, because she had to go downstreet. I knew.

She came back in a half hour. The minute she walked

in, she said, "John, put the sign on the door. Please, please, hurry."

"The sign" was a little piece of cardboard that said, "Back in Five Minutes. Please Wait." It was used most rarely. I was shaking when I put it on the door.

"Come on, John," my mother said, and I followed her to the back of the store and into the parlor. She made me sit down next to her on the couch and she took my two hands. We were all alone. "Dixie Sullivan told me about the bill," she said. "Something kept me from telling him about the receipt, John."

"I did it," I said. And I told her how I had lost the money playing pool and had signed Dixie Sullivan's name to the receipt. I could not pull my hands out of my mother's hands.

It has taken me many years to know fully about those few minutes that followed, and the heart and attitude of my mother. It has taken me many years to realize that there was no word of chastisement from my mother, who is dead now, but only a hope of protecting me.

"So Dixie Sullivan doesn't know," my mother said. "John, John, John! Nobody knows. Whatever you do, John, don't tell a single soul about this. It's terrible, John, but it's all right. I'll pay Dixie Sullivan. Don't tell anybody, whatever you do. Don't even tell your Uncle Will."

All this goes to show why the pool-table people are wasting their time and money trying to convince me that I shouldn't feel sinful about playing pool. Not that it isn't an interesting game.

PART III

Happenings in New York

1

Can't Slip Any Drugs to Sisters
on Fifth Avenue

A NUN stumbled on the sidewalk on Fifth Avenue, near Forty-seventh Street. There was a bad place in the sidewalk and the nun had stepped on it while walking along with another nun. This happened in the middle of a busy afternoon, and the sidewalks were crowded.

A man in a yellow polo coat grabbed the nun's arm, helpfully. The other nun grasped her other arm and looked into her face, which was pale. The two nuns were not used to crowds and milling around, and both looked scared over the trivial mishap.

The man jerked his hat off before he spoke, solicitously, to the nun who had stumbled. He had a cauliflower ear and his hat was a Madison Square Garden kind of hat.

"Is something the matter, Sister?" he said, leaning toward the nun. "Something happen? You hurt yourself, Sister?"

The nun spoke so softly, out of embarrassment, that the man could not hear what she said. Another man, with his hat off, was there by then, and the two nuns and two men made a small clump in the middle of the busy sidewalk. Still another man stood still, only a few feet away, watching them.

"Begging your pardon, Sister," the cauliflower-ear man said, being very careful to use the highest-class language he could figure out, "I thought something happened you're like in distress. I mean taken or something, or hurt your foot, if you'll excuse me."

From under the black hood and starched linen of her religious garb, the nun looked timidly and kindly at him. "I — I — I slipped," she said, and looked appealingly at the other nun.

"I think Sister is all right now," the other nun said. "Her foot slipped, I think. Are you all right, Sister Veronica?"

"Yes. I twisted my — I twisted my ankle a little," Sister Veronica answered. She took a step or two, carefully. The cauliflower-ear man put on his hat, helped her that step or two, then let go of her arm, and took his hat off as the two nuns went on slowly and anxiously down the Avenue.

"I think she's all right," the second man said to him.

"Jeez, I thought something happen to her, I don't

know what," said the cauliflower-ear man. He put on his hat again, looking back at the departing nuns, then started up the street, almost in stride with the second man.

At that minute, the third man, the onlooker, joined them, and the three moved along, almost as if they had known each other before this.

"Look, see what I got — amyl nitrite," the third man said, opening his gloved hand and showing a capsule in it. "I was just going to slip it to her if she — "

"Slip what to her?" the cauliflower-ear man said, almost angrily, checking his stride.

"The amyl nitrite," the fellow answered. "I have it for my old man. He gets attacks. He got a bad heart, my old man, so I have to have it, and I was right there. I thought the nun maybe had a heart at—"

"Whaddaya mean slip it to her? You ain't going to slip no amble nitrites to her," the cauliflower-ear man said. "You ain't slipping no drugs to no nuns on Fifth Avenue. Whaddaya mean?"

"My father," the fellow said, and by now all three were walking together again up the sidewalk, "he's liable to collapse any minute while I'm with him. So I got this — Look, it's to keep your heart going if you get a heart attack like my father does." He showed the capsule again, and then put it back in his coat pocket.

"Yeh, I know what he means," said the other man. "He thought maybe the Sister had a heart attack, and he wanted — "

"Oh, oh," the cauliflower-ear man said, but only partly

satisfied, it seemed by the tone of his voice and the way he looked at the amyl-nitrite man.

"Oh, yes. Yes, that's what I thought. She maybe had a heart attack when I saw you two there helping her. I meant I was ready to slip her the amyl nitrite and bring her to," the man said.

"Yuh? But what if it wasn't?" the cauliflower-ear man asked, only a little placated. "Maybe something else instead of heart attack and that stuff be exactly the wrong thing to slip her? I don't like the idea, slipping drugs to Sisters on Fifth Avenue. You can't go slipping drugs to Sisters on Fifth Avenue, what I mean."

"I can tell if it would be the right thing," the man said. "My father —"

"I see't you mean, you meant well all right, but I don't like the idea slipping even well-meant drugs to a Sister on Fifth Avenue," the cauliflower-ear man said. Then, just before he turned west, he summed it up. "Anyway, the Sister made out all right. All's well ends well."

"Yeah. So long," the amyl-nitrite man said, turning the other way at the corner. "Just the same, lucky I was there, in case it was a heart attack. That stuff I showed you save my old man's life many a time. So long."

The cauliflower-ear man went west, the amyl-nitrite man went east, and the third man went straight on up the Avenue, looking back, but there was no sign of the two nuns, who were a couple blocks away by then, probably.

2

~~~~~~

Third Avenue Medicine

~~~~~~

THERE'S A KIND OF MEDICINE practiced by old veteran bartenders among old veteran drinkers along Third Avenue, not tourists, and probably the Mayo Brothers out in Rochester have never got wind of it.

Perhaps it isn't exactly medicine, but it's medical observation, anyway, and the main part of it is summed up in two things they say at the proper times. One is "The snake is out." The other, which they say in reverent tones, is "The elevens are up." Neither of these sayings has anything to do with the ordinary, everyday bartender school of medicine, which has to do with overpowering a hang-over.

First of all, about the snake. The snake is an ordinary little vein, or maybe it is an artery, that runs along the left temple of a man's head. Most of the time you don't see it, but it's there, and it runs along, a little slant-wise, from up around his hair to above the left-hand corner of his eye.

Take a man gets in his late thirties, into his forties, and then, of course, as time goes on, into his fifties, and he still keeps coming into this saloon or that, wherever he always goes, and after a while this vein, the snake, gets to acting up.

One day this man goes on drinking one after the other — nobody is talking about beer but about hard stuff, and especially, out of all, brandy. No use trying to tell him to take it easy; that only gets him sore and he probably says, "Nobody's going to tell me take it easy, I know what I'm doing, I know what I'm doing," and all that kind of guff.

But after a while — and it has to be understood the bartender is his true friend — why, the bartender leans over the bar and takes a good look at him, staring.

"What's the matter with you?" the man probably says. "Have you gone nuts, looking at me like I was some kind of a bug sitting on a leaf? Give me some more of the same. The glass is empty."

"Oh, no, I'm not nuts," the bartender will say, but not for anyone else to hear. "I was just going to tell you the snake is out."

"Oh, oh!" says the man. "The little son of a bitch come out of his hole, did he?"

And he leans over the bar and stares hard into the mirror. Or if he can't see well that far, he's almost sure to go back in the men's room and study his forehead in the mirror. There will be the snake, pulsing and beating away. It must be blood pressure or something.

Time and time again this happens, in a quiet way, and it seldom fails that it halts up the man that's drinking — slows him up, anyway — when no amount of talk or lecturing could do it. Mostly, they come back from the men's room and tell the barkeep they guess they'll take a little walk, and go over to the park and sit for a while, or else they might even go home and lie down. That's what the snake coming out of his hole does, although it's probably nothing serious in the minds of regular doctors.

"The elevens are up" is as serious as anything could be, and there is no joke about it. This is not said to a man to his face at all. It comes about when there's been an old codger around for years and years, long enough to have arguments about is he seventy-one years old or is he up to seventy-eight or even more. Everybody talks of how healthy he is and he can go on for years yet, as the saying has it.

Then one time comes along and he doesn't drop in for a few days or a week. Everyone (except the tourists, of course) asks for him and someone passes word he's under the weather a little. Then he shows up one day, usually when there's only one or two in there. Such a man, in such a fix, hardly ever comes bouncing back into the place while the crowd is there. He visits for a few minutes and says he's all right, a little weak, but he'll be all right in a week or so, and then he leaves.

No sooner has he gone than those of his friends who are there — including the bartender, of course — look at each other.

"The elevens are up," says the bartender, quietly and sadly, like a priest or a judge or the like.

"They are, they are!" say the others, and they all nod their heads.

It means that the two cords on the back of the man's neck have begun to stick out, the way they have never stuck out before his illness. The space on each side of each cord has sunk away — wasted, you might say — so the two cords, from his collar to his hair, stick out like two "1"s, making a number "11." That's why they say "The elevens are up" when it happens to an old codger. It means he hasn't a chance and there's not much more time for him. They never let him hear them saying it, but the word passes around, one to another, and for a little while everyone is nicer than usual to the man, until what they're sure will happen does happen.

3

The Television Helps,
but Not Very Much

Wʜᴇɴ I got into the cab to go down from Seventy-second and Second to Forty-fourth and Fifth, it seemed stuffy, so I gave the handle a twist and let the window down a little.

"That's all right," the driver said. "I'll take and close this here one up, if it's all right with you."

"Oh, sure," I said.

"If they're both open, it makes a draft on the back of my neck," he explained, nicely. "I ought to be home, I got a cold."

"That's about all you can do for these colds," I said.

"Go to bed is the best thing," he said. "Only with me, maybe I'm better off milling around in the hack. Too lonesome home. I lost my wife."

"Oh," I said. "Was it recently it happened? I mean when did she die?"

"Pretty near a year ago at that," he said.

We were moving along Seventy-second, getting near Fifth. Traffic was slow even before we hit Fifth.

Some of them are gabby, the hack drivers. This one wasn't, even though it turned out we talked all the way. It didn't seem to be gab. It seemed natural talk, almost as if we had known each other a long while.

"I got myself a television," he said. "For company like. The television helps, but not very much, at that."

"No kids or anything?" I asked.

"No, we didn't," he said. "We didn't have any children at all. No in-laws, even. See, we come from another city here. More than twenty years here. We made out all right. It ain't the best job in the world, but we battle along all right together, twenty years. Long time."

"Yes," I said.

"Like I say about the television, I can get interested, all right, like a fight or even sometimes those cowboy movies they put on. Just the same, sooner or later the television got to wind up, don't it? I mean, it comes to the end of whatever the show is or wrassling or whatever it is."

"I know what you mean. The thing goes off," I said.

"Yeah, the thing winds up and there I am again," he said. "I'm alone again and I maybe go to the icebox and get a beer, but it's lonesome. Do you think it wouldn't be so bad if I had kids somewheres? Even if they were grown-up somewheres?"

"I don't know," I said. "I don't have any children."

"They say it's different if you have kids," he said. "Even if you lose your wife. That's what they say."

"Some people say that," I said. "I don't know. Did she die suddenly?"

"She was sick about two weeks, that's all," he said. "But the more I think about it, she must have been sick a long while. The doctor said she must have been. She didn't like to have doctors. Matter of fact, it was me got him finally. And I had to go to him and say to him, look, I said to him, she's going to be sore at you coming in. I said, she's against you before she even lays an eye on you, I says, so please don't mind if she acts sore. Later on, after it's all over, he tells me it was too late, the thing that was the matter with her it was too late to do anything."

"That was tough," I said.

"Thing is I keep worrying," he said. "Was it my fault maybe I wasn't more bossy and make her get a doctor? What do you think? I worry about it all the time. Like that's why I didn't stay home with this damn cold. I'd be around the house thinking maybe we'd be together just the same as always, me coming home and having supper and help with the dishes and we both sit down and have a couple beers, listen to the radio, if I made her get a doctor and never mind how much beefing, squawking she do about it. What do you think?"

"Oh, I don't know," I said. "That's a tough one to answer." It wasn't that I wanted to give the driver a short answer, but there I was, thrown into the middle of a man's life, and I didn't know the man.

"You're telling me it's a tough one!" he said. "Just the same, I got the notion you're kind of sensible, and after all, what harm is there? Like I tell you, I got no in-laws, no kids, I had an idea I'd talk it over with somebody. Them guys around the garage, what the hell, they're dumber than me, even. What do they know? Know what I mean?"

"Yes," I said.

"Like, the truth of the matter, I could get married again right away," he said. "Those guys all said don't be a sucker — don't be a sucker, they said."

"About what?" I asked.

"Well, might as well out with it," he said. "There's this girl I could get married with. Do you think I look forty-eight?"

"I don't know," I said. "I hardly looked at you much. Just got in the cab, hardly looked at anything except that it was a cab."

"I guess I look forty-eight all right," he said. "Well, this girl is thirty-one. She has a little baby. I met her at a guy's house; he had me there eating Christmas. Didn't want me eating in a coffeepot first Christmas I had no wife, he said."

"She divorced or what, the girl with the baby?" I asked.

"No," he said. "Thing is she was a Wac — you know, in the war they had women they called them Wacs. She was in Chicago and she married this fellow, and it's only three months after and he dies on her. So in a little while she had the baby, and that's the way it is. She's a very nice woman, only seventeen years younger. I mean seventeen years younger than me. I told you I'm forty-eight, didn't I? Well, this girl, or maybe I should say woman, she's thirty-one and got the baby and thirty-one from forty-eight, that's seventeen, see what I mean?"

"Yes," I said.

"The guys at the garage say that's too much difference, and with the kid and all," he said. "What they don't understand is I like the kid, see what I mean? I bought the kid a couple toys, and you should see how this girl appreciated it I bought toys for the kid. Don't think for a minute this is any kind of a fly-around dame. She's nice. She lives with her mother now, and she works when she can get work."

"I bet she's all right," I said.

"You can say that again," he said. "Just between ourselves, she proposed to me, you might say. Know what I mean? Honest to God, it ain't this sex stuff, that ain't the main thing at all, no matter what the guys in the garage say; they're always harping about that angle. What I mean is — well, I would like to have her around, kid and all. I like the kid. He ain't very big yet, but he could look at the television, too. Like I say, it helps keep me from getting so goddam lonesome but it don't take care of things altogether, know what I mean? Will you tell me one thing? I mean, I want you give me your opinion — it's pretty near Forty-fourth Street after we get this light."

"O.K., what is it?" I said.

"Never mind the guys in the garage — do *you* think

it'd be all right if we got married? You think it would work out?"

"You're coming at me rather suddenly with this," I said, sparring for time.

"I know," he said. "I don't say I'll do what you tell me, but just the same, you got an idea now how things are, don't you?"

"Well, I think I understand," I said.

"O.K., then, what do you think?"

"All right, you asked me," I said, and drew a deep breath. "I say go ahead and get married. That's what I say, sight unseen."

"Right!" he said, speaking almost loud for the first time in our rolling acquaintance. "That settles it. I guess I only needed somebody, anybody, say go ahead. Like give me a little shove, you might say. I'm going to do it. It's too goddam lonesome. And I like the kid, no fooling. This is Forty-fourth. Do you want this corner or the downtown side?"

"This corner's all right," I said, and got out and hollered back, "Good luck!"

"O.K., doc," he said. He was smiling, and now I guess he'll go ahead and get married. Probably never see him again. I didn't even look at his name beside the picture in the frame, but I hope they make out all right.